Cause and Effect
LEAN

Lean Operations, Six Sigma and Supply Chain Essentials

John Bicheno

PICSIE Books

PRODUCTION AND INVENTORY CONTROL, SYSTEMS AND INDUSTRIAL ENGINEERING BOOKS

Buckingham, England
Copyright 2000

ISBN 0 9513 8301 9

CONTENTS

Foreword

Much has happened in Lean since the publication six years ago of the second edition of Cause and Effect JIT. Womack and Jones have articulated the five principles of Lean Thinking, Six Sigma has come into its own, supply chain thinking has developed significantly, the concept of Kaizen and Kaizen blitz has moved forward, 5S is well established, and measurement has taken huge strides forward.

This new edition incorporates these and other improvements, while still retaining the successful cause and effect diagram format. The aim remains to give readers a fast yet full overview of lean operations. As before, the book is not intended to be a complete reference work on Lean operations but rather a quick reference guide.

As noted in the second edition, there is for many still a long way to go. I am still worried when I hear of companies that claim to have "done" Lean or JIT. We have all just started. We all need to wear our "muda" spectacles and to continue to "peel the onion".

John Bicheno
September 2000

A note on the cover design:-

The cover represents the convergence of the three most significant developments in operations. The central band is Lean and converges from streams in the West and Japan, leaving behind the "black hole" of batch and queue and mass production. The cover design is also reminiscent of the flag of South Africa, where the author was born.

WORLD CLASS PRIORITIES

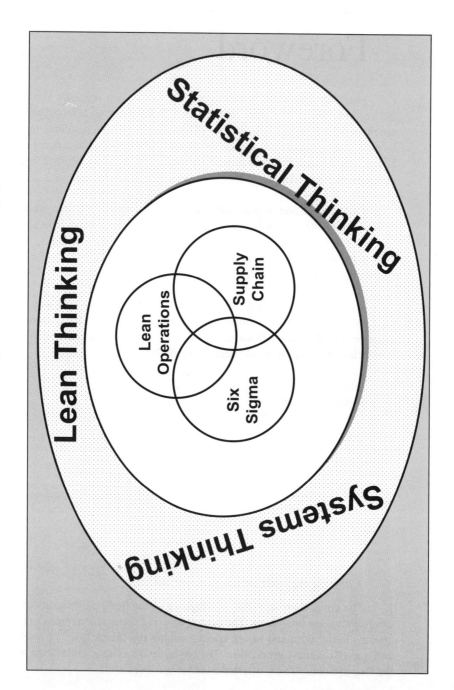

THE LEAN SCORECARD

Priorities

Three principal priorities for operations in the new millennium are Lean operations, Six Sigma quality and Supply Chain management. These interlink. They also need to be embedded in a background of three related forms of thinking.

LEAN THINKING.

Lean thinking is a philosophy not a system or a technique. It is about simplicity, flow, visibility, partnership, and value. Womack and Jones' Lean Thinking emphasises the elimination of waste and the adoption of five lean principles.

1. Specify value from the point of view of the customer.
2. Identify the value stream (mapping is a powerful way to do this). Concentrate on the object not the organisational department. There are three streams to be mapped, the physical flow, the information flow, and new product introduction. In each there will be value adding activities, non-value adding activities, and temporarily necessary non-value adding activities. Improve the first, eliminate the second, and reduce the third.
3. Make value flow. If possible use one piece flow. Avoid batch and queue. Remove all obstacles that prevent flow from taking place.
4. Pull at the customer's rate of demand. Use one, make one. This extends to the full supply chain. Seek to avoid over-production.
5. Seek perfection through continual improvement and the steady adoption of the first four principles.

The family of lean techniques described in this book support the adoption of these key principles.

SYSTEMS THINKING.

Systems Thinking, with origins in biology a century or more ago, only began to have an impact on management during the last thirty or so years. It is the basis of process reengineering and the internet. It is also fundamental to Lean, which is ultimately a systems philosophy.

8

A system is a set of entities together with the relationship between them. Think of a children's mobile – touch one element and the whole thing moves. So it is with management systems. There is ecology at work.

A central tenant is the process view. Think in terms of end-to-end processes that deliver the products and services customers require, rather than vertical departmental "silos". Some processes will be core and some support. The process view is integral in process reengineering, in total quality, in lean thinking, and in supply chain thinking.

Human activity systems generally have a goal or purpose around which the entities or activities are organised. Systems have clients and customers, beneficiaries and victims. They contain resources (people, materials, and machines) which are joined together by information flows to support the goals. Systems contain sub-systems with all the characteristics of the higher level system. Trying to optimise a sub system on its own is futile and may be counterproductive. Systems grow, decline and interact with their environment; they are only self-sustaining together with their environment; they affect the environment and the environment affects them. Feedback and control are parts of every system, the effectiveness of which has a major impact on the ability to achieve the goals.

The concept of Learning is central in Systems Thinking. Natural systems learn by evolution. Management systems also learn by experience but this may be too slow. They need to set out to learn specifically about themselves, their operations, their processes, and their customers.

An important idea in Systems Thinking is feedback loops. Positive feedback grows like interest in a bank. Negative feedback is goal seeking like a thermostat. Most systems contain both types of loop. The point is, understanding the loops is essential to managing systems behaviour. A classic case is the so-called Forrester Effect in Supply Chains resulting in demand amplification.

Systems Thinking teaches that effective ways to manage systems is to decrease response time, not to attack positive feedback (work harder), but to go for negative feedback (prevention), and to work in systems or processes rather than in "silo". In other words get to the root cause.

9

QUALITY and SIX SIGMA Linkages

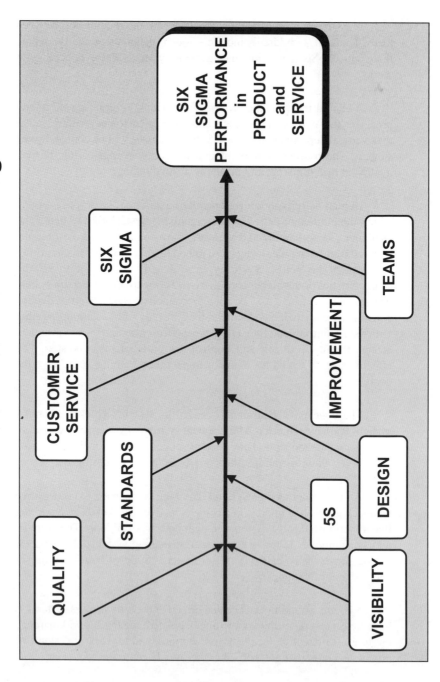

STATISTICAL THINKING.

Statistical thinking recognises that variation is everywhere. The key task is to understand and reduce variation, to manage it, but it cannot be eliminated. Deming said that a prime failure of management was their inability to understand variation. Consider why so many management "solutions" (MRP, TQM, and even some Lean) do not work – ignoring variation is a big reason.

Statistical thinking overlaps with Systems Thinking in as far as both recognise that all work should be viewed as a process, and all processes are inter connected. Data is needed to guide decisions, and such data should include measurement of variation. Avoid "drowning in a river of average depth one metre".

One needs to aware of the differences between common cause variation and special cause variation. Treating common causes as special causes (known as tinkering) can make the situation far worse. Unlearning the deterministic view of the world is a great challenge.

LEAN OPERATIONS

Lean has a long history, although not called "lean" until 1990. Henry Ford was a lean pioneer at Highland Park. Deming taught the Japanese about waste. Boeing made bombers using lean during World War II. Taiichi Ohno and Toyota refined lean over 30 years. Today many of the most exciting lean companies (Dell, Nypro, Volvo, HP, TRW, etc.) are once again to be found in the West. Yet some are still to start. The time is now short.

Lean has been slow to expand out of manufacturing. But the signs are now strong in construction, in health, even in law firms. The future is bright. Hence "operations" not "manufacturing".

SIX SIGMA

Six Sigma and lean have in common reduction of variation and improvement in performance. In operations, variation is the supreme killer.

Six Sigma began in Motorola in 1987 as an alternative to less successful TQM. The roots, in variation, go back to Deming. In 1995 Jack

SUPPLY CHAIN Linkages

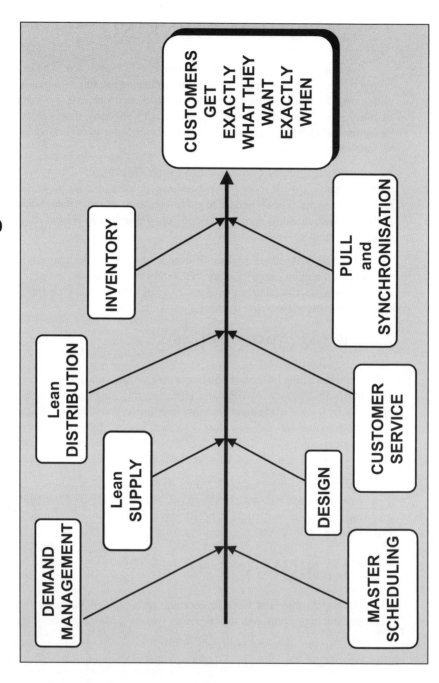

Welsh who supported it at GE gave the concept a big boost. Today there is vast experience in both service and manufacturing. Six Sigma is pragmatic with strong links to the bottom line. It is based around process and variation, uses well-established statistical concepts, has a clear methodology, and a recognised practitioner route (through "black belt" training).

Six Sigma is not just about product quality. It is about quality in its widest sense – quality of process (both core and support), of service, and of product. Ultimately it is about winning and retaining customers.

Quality and Lean are close partners, mutually reinforcing one another. Their future together seems assured.

SUPPLY CHAIN

"Supply Chains compete, not companies". Today the great opportunities for reducing lead-time, cutting waste, cutting inventory, and improving flexibility through the supply chain are becoming well recognised. Improving the supply chain means, in the first instance, extending the principles lean and six sigma to all participants in the chain. A chain is only as good as its weakest link. But with that foundation, there are further massive opportunities by calling in the particular strengths of partners, by sharing information about customers, and providing agility at the most appropriate parts of the chain. The internet, B2B and B2C, is the great facilitator.

The world class trilogy is the way forward.

Lean STAGE 1

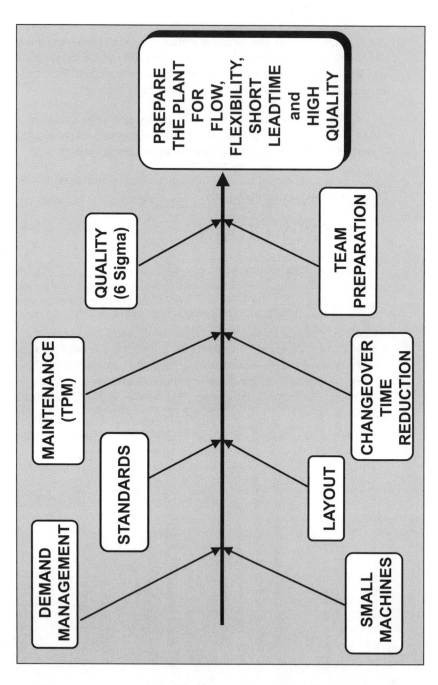

Lean STAGE 2

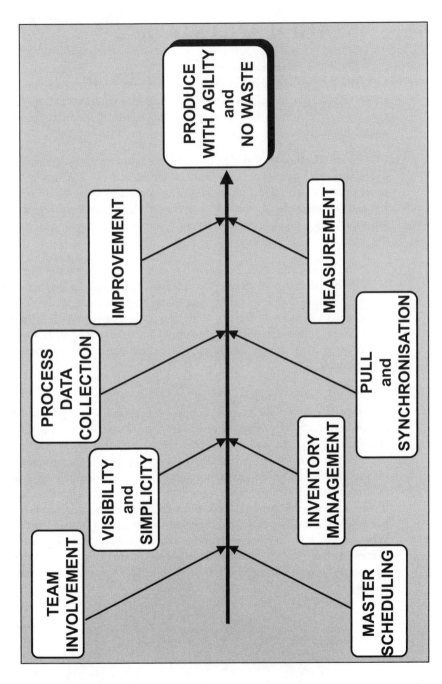

STAGE 1 AND STAGE 2

Stage 1 is about preparing for Lean. The full set of principles and techniques outlined in stage 1 are applicable in all operations organisations, irrespecitve of size or volume. You should be active in all these areas. All are good common sense. They form the basis of manufacturing competitiveness.

Stage 2 is the set of principles and techniques for actually running operations in a Lean away. They build on the stage 1 set, and very often require some of the stage 1 techniques to be in place in order to minimise risk and maximise effectiveness. Most are applicable in every organisation, but some may be less applicable where volumes were low or variety is high.

The Stage 1 and Stage 2 concept is a guide to implementation. But it is not the intention that all stage 1 principles should be implemented before starting on stage 2. Rather, going lean is an ongoing cyclic process of improvement. Actions in stage 1 allow actions in stage 2 which in turn allow further actions in stage 2, and so on. At any time several stage 1 and stage 2 principles may be in the process of implementation of further improvement.

As an example, reducing set- up times (stage 1) allows buffers to be cut (stage 2), which could then mean opportunities for layout improvement (stage 1), thereby improving the opportunities for visibility and flow scheduling (stage 2), and so on. This emphasises that every time an improvement is made we should then look out for further improvements in other areas that have been made possible as a result. To do this, everyone must participate in identifying the opportunities. Many small improvements involving wide participation is more effective than a few big improvements put in by "experts" or outsiders, especially if these tend to disintegrate. When improvement is done effectively, year in year out, both within the plant and in its supply and distribution environment, the competitive advantage become enormous. Hence this booklet to assist you in your journey.

Lean and POLICY DEPLOYMENT

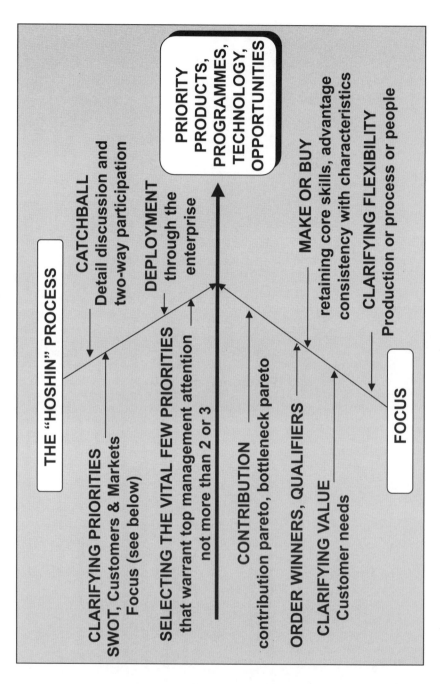

THE "HOSHIN" PROCESS

CLARIFYING PRIORITIES
SWOT, Customers & Markets
Focus (see below)

CATCHBALL
Detail discussion and
two-way participation

DEPLOYMENT
through the
enterprise

SELECTING THE VITAL FEW PRIORITIES
that warrant top management attention
not more than 2 or 3

PRIORITY
PRODUCTS,
PROGRAMMES,
TECHNOLOGY,
OPPORTUNITIES

CONTRIBUTION
contribution pareto, bottleneck pareto

MAKE OR BUY
retaining core skills, advantage
consistency with characteristics

ORDER WINNERS, QUALIFIERS

CLARIFYING FLEXIBILITY
Production or process or people

CLARIFYING VALUE
Customer needs

FOCUS

Stage 1

POLICY DEPLOYMENT

HOSHIN.
The Japanese name for policy deployment now adopted increasingly by lean companies to guide operations strategy.

Clarifying Priorities and SWOT Analysis is generally the first step. This involves conventional strategic management steps.

Selecting the Vital Few. Hoshin (from a Japanese word meaning Helmsman) believes that top management should be concerned with a few priorities only. Steering the tanker, but the rest of the ship can run itself. Hence 2 or 3 areas for attention to change. Change is so vital, but also difficult, so should not be confused with ongoing operations.

Catchball. Once top level priorities are decided they are discussed, level by level, throughout the organisation. Detail is added. Feedback is given. Refinements are made.

Deployment. Final policies are deployed level by level throughout the organisation. Measure development is an important part; each level setting its own measures that contribute to the achievement of higher level measures.

FOCUS.
An important set of strategic decisions that have to be made whether or not there is a Hoshin process in operation. Achieving focus is a pre-requisite to lean operations.

Contribution. Do a Pareto analysis of product contribution. Frequently a long tail of products that make little or negative contribution is found. Use this to think about product line rationalisation. In companies with important bottleneck processes, do an analysis by contribution per bottleneck minute used. The last thing you want is products making very low contribution but which also tie up your precious bottleneck process.

Lean and DEMAND MANAGEMENT

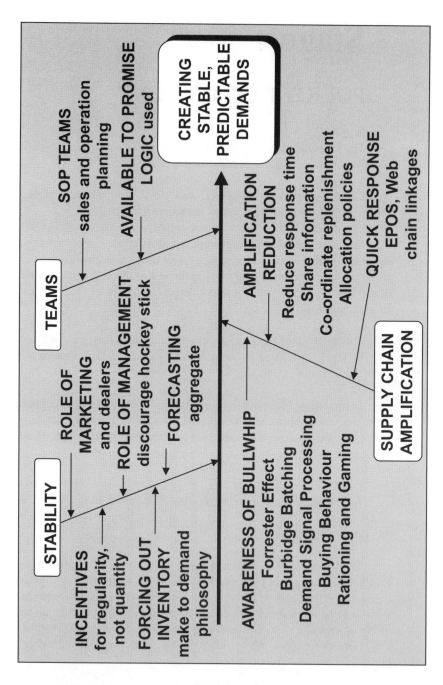

STABILITY

TEAMS

INCENTIVES
for regularity, not quantity

FORCING OUT INVENTORY
make to demand philosophy

ROLE OF MARKETING
and dealers

ROLE OF MANAGEMENT
discourage hockey stick

FORECASTING
aggregate

SOP TEAMS
sales and operation planning

AVAILABLE TO PROMISE
LOGIC used

CREATING STABLE, PREDICTABLE DEMANDS

AWARENESS OF BULLWHIP
Forrester Effect
Burbidge Batching
Demand Signal Processing
Buying Behaviour
Rationing and Gaming

AMPLIFICATION REDUCTION
Reduce response time
Share information
Co-ordinate replenishment
Allocation policies

QUICK RESPONSE
EPOS, Web chain linkages

SUPPLY CHAIN AMPLIFICATION

Order Winners, Order Qualifiers. Ask what do we need to do to get into the stadium (qualifiers) and what do we need to do to win the game (winners). Hence make sure that operations are capable of delivering.

Clarifying value. One definition of value is performance / cost. What is it that customers value in your products and services. Some mix of cost, quality, delivery, flexibility, speed, service. People, process and capacity decisions depend upon this knowledge.

Make or Buy. Unlike Henry Ford most companies cannot make everything. So what to make or buy depends upon answers to the above questions, plus considerations such as retention of core skills both now and in future, capability to make what customer's want, and avoiding operations complexity.

DEMAND MANAGEMENT.

Lean works best when there is a uniform flow of products right along the chain. This will never be perfect, but the purpose of demand management is to make sure that flow is as regular as possible.

STABILITY.
Stability of schedules is the aim. There should be no incentives that create demand amplification. For instance, quantity discounts encourage the buying of unneeded quantities in the short term. Rather give discounts for regular orders. Forcing out inventory discourages accountants and others from playing games with inventory to massage the balance sheet. Marketing has an important role to play by encouraging demand when it is low and discouraging when it is high. Management should adopt practices that discourage the end of month "hockey stick". One possibility is to stagger end-of-month dates for salesmen. Forecasting by family and then breaking down the forecast into product groups discourages unrealistic demands.

TEAMS
Sales and operation planning teams encourage looking at demands from both aspects. Available to promise logic gives a good indication to sales of the available capacity and encourages stability.

Lean and TOTAL MAINTENANCE

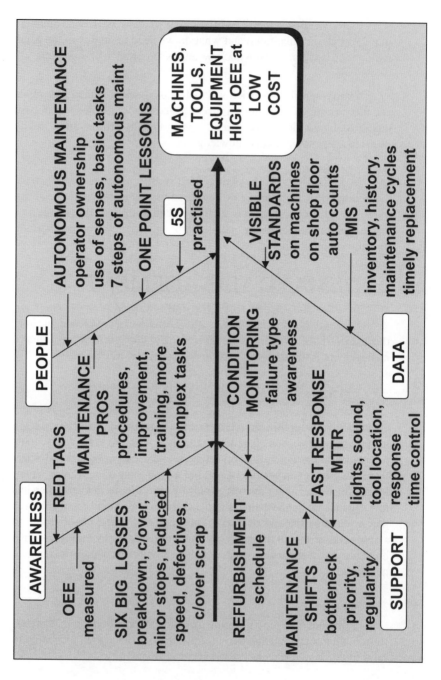

AWARENESS

OEE measured

SIX BIG LOSSES
breakdown, c/over, minor stops, reduced speed, defectives, c/over scrap

RED TAGS

PEOPLE

MAINTENANCE PROS
procedures, improvement, training, more complex tasks

AUTONOMOUS MAINTENANCE
operator ownership
use of senses, basic tasks
7 steps of autonomous maint

ONE POINT LESSONS

5S practised

REFURBISHMENT schedule

CONDITION MONITORING
failure type awareness

VISIBLE STANDARDS
on machines
on shop floor
auto counts
MIS
inventory, history, maintenance cycles
timely replacement

MAINTENANCE SHIFTS
bottleneck priority, regularity

FAST RESPONSE
MTTR
lights, sound, tool location, response time control

SUPPORT

DATA

MACHINES, TOOLS, EQUIPMENT HIGH OEE at LOW COST

SUPPLY CHAIN AMPLIFICATION.

This is where, at each stage along the supply or distribution chain, demand instability increases. The first step towards elimination is understanding. The causes of this so-called Bullwhip or Forrester effect are: (a) the Burbidge effect that results from batching decisions that translate uniform demands into lumpy demands. These lumpy demands become ever more pronounced. (b) Demand signal instability occurs when members of the chain read the signals or forecasts incorrectly and put in orders to the next stage to anticipate these false signals. (c) Buying behaviour instability results from taking advantage of quantity discounts or in anticipation of price rises that cause false demand patterns. (d) Rationing and gaming are policies adopted by suppliers for apparent short-term advantage. Rationing involves creating false shortages and gaming involves for instance building up inventory in anticipation of year-end. If suppliers know that demands are increasing and shortages likely they may exaggerate their orders.

Amplification reduction involves one or more of the following. (a) A reduction in response time so that forecasts are more accurate or can be eliminated. (b) Sharing information right along the chain enables true demands to be communicated. Uniform schedules can then be agreed. (c) The co ordination of replenishment inventory prevents false demands from being communicated. All members of the chain should be made aware of ways in which replenishment systems operate so as to prevent false interpretation of demands.

Quick response and efficient consumer response, pioneered in the grocery and apparel industries, encourages direct links with electronic point of sale with demands communicated immediately along the chain. This is combined with design and distribution actions – see separate sections.

TOTAL MAINTENANCE

For lean, machines, tools and equipment have to be available without fail when needed. Of course, cost is also important but if everyone participates, these two aims are not trade-offs. The phrase total productive maintenance emphasises that the concept goes beyond prevention to include improvement in productivity. Total productive maintenance has much in common with total quality. That is, both encourage participation by both experts and operators, both emphasise ownership, both take a process view, and both rely on good housekeeping.

AWARENESS. The starting point.

OEE or overall equipment effectiveness is defined as availability % x performance rate % x yield rate %. This is a comprehensive view. Many companies display OEE graphs near critical machines; an overall graph and three supporting graphs, one for each factor. Below may be shown fishbone diagrams of contributing causes. Some management insist on OEE data before authorising capital expenditure; it may be better to improve rather than buy.

Six Big Losses are the elements of OEE. Awareness helps prioritise.

Red Tags provide visible awareness of maintenance requirements. Tags, sometimes with dates, are hung on a board and returned to the machine when the required maintenance is complete. Immediate visual impact of backlog.

PEOPLE. TPM is ultimately a people programme.

Autonomous Maintenance means operator responsibility for own machines and for operators carrying out as much routine maintenance work as possible. However, autonomous does not mean voluntary. People come with built-in noise detection, vision, and vibration detection equipment. So use these precious capabilities and get operators to report anything unusual. 5S (see separate section) is an excellent way to involve people in TPM. Note: the term "autonomous maintenance" is used by Japan Institute of Plant Maintenance and includes 7 steps: cleanup, stop sources of defects, formulate standards, overall checkup, inside checkup, orderliness and tidiness, and ongoing improvement – roughly similar to 5S.

One-point lessons are TPM learning points for operators, where just one point is covered on a chart or sheet of paper. Focused learning. They are applicable not only in maintenance.

Maintenance professionals should do the more skilled tasks. As they do this, OEE performance increases and a positive feedback loop is established. Freeing time should allow more operator training, and so on. The maintenance professionals in consultation with operators should work out standard procedures.

SUPPORT.

Maintenance Shifts are a possibility in non-7/24 operations but routine maintenance is essential everywhere. Bottlenecks should enjoy priority. A regular cycle of preventive maintenance should be maintained and recorded where appropriate (below).

A refurbishment plan, aiming to go beyond just routine preventive maintenance, where machines enjoy a new lease of life, is developed in accordance with usage.

Condition Monitoring, a relatively new activity monitors characteristics such as vibration and oil content to predict maintenance requirements. Failure type awareness is important for preventive maintenance – some machines have a "bathtub" failure mode, others L shaped, others flat, others reverse L. Knowing the failure mode determines whether PM is a good idea and when to do it.

Fast Response and Mean Time to Repair are possibly more important than mean time to failure because variation is reduced. Hence monitor and record MTTR. Use red tags. Use light and sound to draw attention (Toyota plays operator-selected tunes). Tool location should reflect frequency of use.

DATA.
Visible Standards for maintenance should be kept by machines, using photographs and sketches. Even better, show normal settings on the machine itself. Use automatic part counters to change tools and replace parts with a known frequency.

Information Systems play an important role to record breakdown and problem data for subsequent improvement target actions or optimal replacement decisions.

TOTAL QUALITY

Quality works in partnership with lean. As lean is implemented, quality improves and vice versa. Why? Because improved visibility, regularity, smaller batches, reduced space, less inventory, and so on all directly impact quality. And improving quality makes pull systems and scheduling work better. Apart from cost and waste, improving quality is about reducing the great enemy – variation.

PREVENTION
A fundamental idea of quality management – is more cost effective than inspection and much cheaper than failure.

Statistical Process Control is a prevention approach with the SPC goal of stable, predictable and capable processes. SPC charts should be kept lineside. The goal should always be to continually improve the

Lean and TOTAL QUALITY

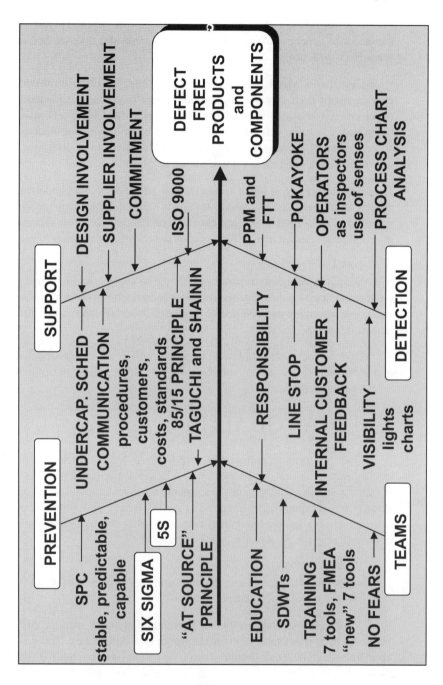

capability index Cpk. Inspect the process, not the product. And SPC charts are powerful in distinguishing common causes from special causes. Tinkering with the former simply makes things worse.

Six Sigma is dealt with on a separate page. It should not be thought of as replacing total quality, but as one powerful means to achieve improvement. Likewise 5S.

The "At Source Principle" is that quality problems should be dealt with right there and then. Operator responsibility. Never knowingly pass on a defective.

Taguchi Methods, also known as design of experiments, allow one to home in on the most quality critical variables economically and rapidly. Shainin methods are a variation, to search for the "Red X". Shainin methods range from simple to sophisticated, and are powerful. Both Shainin and Taguchi deserve wider attention.

SUPPORT

Undercapacity Scheduling. If capacity is scheduled to 100% of time there will be no time to correct errors or make improvements. So schedule deliberately under full capacity to take the pressure off and allow initiative and decision making to happen – also to guarantee to hit the schedule.

Communication of correct procedures from designers and engineers is required. Spend as much time as is needed. "Sit by Nelly". Use sketches and photos to communicate standards. Some allow operators to talk directly with customers and suppliers.

Deming's 85/15 principle states that 85% of quality problems are ultimately traceable to management, only 15% to operators. Poor specs, poor training, unclear requirements are typical causes.

Design Involvement means perhaps 80% of defects eliminated before they even get to the line. Think design for assembly (DFA) for ease of assembly, and Toyota sending a design team to live in California, near customers, for the Lexus product concept. Supplier involvement also is good for simplification. Close the communication gap between design and manufacture.

Commitment (one of Oakland's 3 C's of Culture, Communication, Commitment) on the part of managers is required. Inspirational examples abound: Galvin at Motorola, Welsh at GE, Egan at Jaguar.

ISO9000 is not great at quality improvement, but lays many a foundation for good practice. The year 2000 version shows promise.

Lean and SIX SIGMA

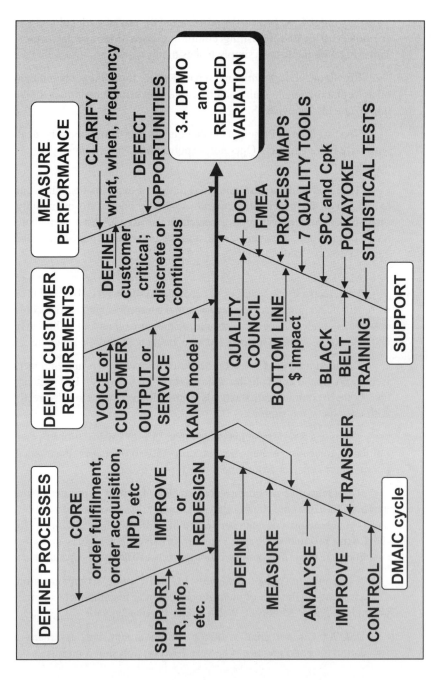

TEAMS

Teams need Education in the 7 basic tools of quality, perhaps in the new tools, and in FMEA and others. See Six Sigma. All this needs to take place in a "no fears" climate – defect detection is good, no one need fear for jobs as a result of improvement. And teams need to take responsibility for quality in their own cells and areas.

DETECTION

Although prevention is the goal, detection is essential. Pokayoke (error proofing) devices carry out 100% automatic checks with either stop or warning when a defect is detected.

Parts per million (ppm) has become a standard measure of quality. This is often measured at the output stage. But first time through (ftt) is a better measure for process quality. This measures the percentage or parts per million that pass through all stages without any rework or scrap. It is quite possible to have a very low ppm rate but a ftt rate of 100% or 1 million.

Operators come with built-in vision. And hearing. Use it. When problems are detected they should be fed back to the source immediately; no delay.

Line Stop (the classic is at Toyota) means operators empowered to stop the line to prevent defects from proceeding. Immediate feedback and real empowerment. Less powerful means use lights and sound but are still good.

Process Chart analysis can give important clues to problems as well as being used for process control.

SIX SIGMA

Six Sigma is about process improvement and goes far beyond product defect rates. It is an ordered, tested methodology for widescale improvement in service and manufacture. Ultimately six sigma is not about quality improvement – it is about improving the bottom line.

DEFINE PROCESSES. The starting point. There are two types of process, "core" and "support" and two approaches "improvement" and "redesign". Core processes enjoy first priority. Note "process" not department. Contractors may provide support processes. In the short term all processes are candidates for improvement, but periodic redesign may be called for. There are different methodologies for each.

Lean and STANDARDS

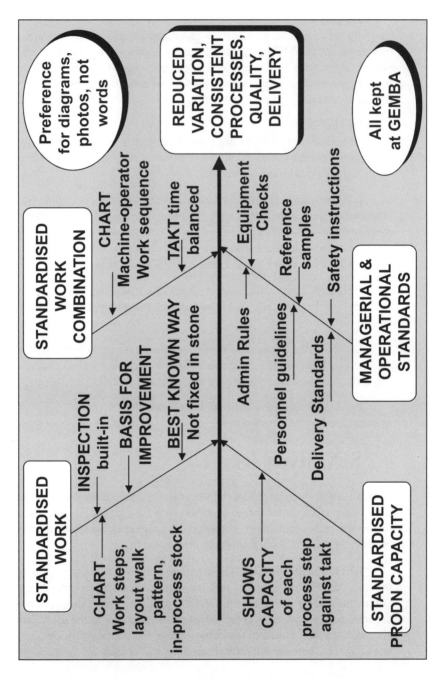

STANDARDISED WORK

CHART
Work steps, layout walk pattern, in-process stock

INSPECTION built-in

BASIS FOR IMPROVEMENT

BEST KNOWN WAY Not fixed in stone

Preference for diagrams, photos, not words

STANDARDISED WORK COMBINATION

CHART
Machine-operator Work sequence

TAKT time balanced

REDUCED VARIATION, CONSISTENT PROCESSES, QUALITY, DELIVERY

All kept at GEMBA

SHOWS CAPACITY of each process step against takt

STANDARDISED PRODN CAPACITY

Admin Rules

Personnel guidelines

Delivery Standards

Equipment Checks

Reference samples

Safety instructions

MANAGERIAL & OPERATIONAL STANDARDS

30

DEFINE CUSTOMER REQUIREMENTS is next. Who are customers of each process and what do they require, value. The Voice of the Customer must be heard through a variety of sources. Requirements may be for an output from the process or for a service as part of the process, typically both. The Kano model (categorising into basics, performance-related, or delighters) is useful.

Then MEASURE PERFORMANCE. Go to gemba. Collect the facts, not opinions. Define the customer critical measures, not the organisation critical measures. Give preference to continuous measures rather than discrete (yes/no) measures. How late, not if late. Take account of variability. Use statistical tests. The measure to be used for each process should be carefully defined in terms of what to measure, where, when and frequency of collection. Calculate the defect opportunities, and hence calculate the defects per million opportunities – Six Sigma aims at 3.5 DPMO and reduced variation. Note variation is a big killer – far better to be consistently one day late with delivery than sometimes one week early, sometimes one week late but OK on average.

Now you can begin the DMAIC cycle. Define, Measure, Analyse, Improve, Control. There are standard steps, questions and procedures for each step depending on whether improvement or redesign is called for. An addition is Transfer – where what is achieved in one area is transferred to others. There may be an intranet for this.

A range of well-established quality and statistical methods provides SUPPORT for Six Sigma. Normally there will be a Quality Council or similar steering group. A feature is strong bottom line linkage to translate improvements into money. And a trained hierarchy of experts, from Green Belt to Master Black Belt undertakes projects.

Note the linkage diagram for six sigma – many areas in this book are relevant.

STANDARDS

Standards are the building blocks for Lean, for Six Sigma, and for the Supply Chain. Continuous improvement needs to "hold the gains" (Juran) before moving forward and standards prevent slipping backwards. We are not talking here about British Standards, MIL standards, ISO standards, Fire Standards and the like. Such standards tend to be fixed and given. We are talking here about operations standards – the current best,

Lean and SMALL MACHINES

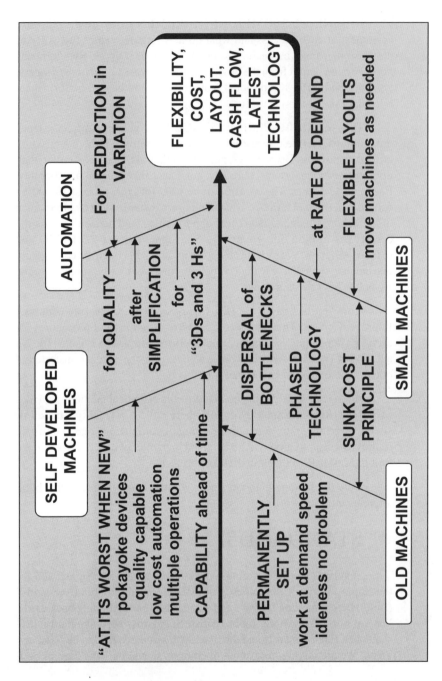

AUTOMATION

For REDUCTION in VARIATION

FLEXIBILITY, COST, LAYOUT, CASH FLOW, LATEST TECHNOLOGY

SELF DEVELOPED MACHINES

for QUALITY

after SIMPLIFICATION

for "3Ds and 3 Hs"

"AT ITS WORST WHEN NEW"
pokayoke devices
quality capable
low cost automation
multiple operations

CAPABILITY ahead of time

DISPERSAL of BOTTLENECKS

PHASED TECHNOLOGY

SUNK COST PRINCIPLE

at RATE OF DEMAND

FLEXIBLE LAYOUTS
move machines as needed

SMALL MACHINES

PERMANENTLY SET UP
work at demand speed
idleness no problem

OLD MACHINES

safest known way. Standards should be written by operators not work experts, revised whenever necessary, followed between revisions, be kept at the workplace (at "Gemba"), making best use of photos and sketches rather than words. There are generally four categories, the first three of which relate together to workplaces or cells.

Any time a standard is not being followed (for instance more than the standard inventory) this indicates that something unusual is happening. Action is called for.

STANDARDISED WORK charts set out the steps carried out by an operator in a process or in making a product. They include work steps, the layout walk pattern in the case of cells, and the standard in-process stock. Standardised work should allow time for inspection, but generally no allowance for rest and delay, which should be taken at specific intervals not continually occurring at unspecified times.

STANDARDISED PRODUCTION CAPACITY turns standard times into the standard daily capacity. This is measured against takt time (the customer's rate of demand).

STANDARDISED WORK COMBINATION Chart is found in cells where operators tend several machines. The chart shows the time to load, unload and walk between machines. Machine cycles are also shown. An operator must be able to complete his work cycle within the takt time. This is the lean form of "man machine chart".

MANAGERIAL AND OPERATIONAL STANDARDS are found at Gemba throughout the rest of the organisation. There may be standards for meetings, for agendas, for delivery, for safety, for most things. This is safety, good management, order, and not bureaucracy.

SMALL MACHINES

The SMALL MACHINE concept is one of the least recognised lean facilitators. The general principle is to use the smallest machine possible consistent with quality requirements. Several smaller machines instead of one bigger, faster one allows flexibility in layouts, easier scheduling, reduction in material handling, less vulnerability to breakdown, less vulnerability to bottleneck problems, possibly reduced cost (through a mix of capability), and through phasing of machine acquisition, improved cash flow and more frequent technology updates.

Lean and LAYOUT

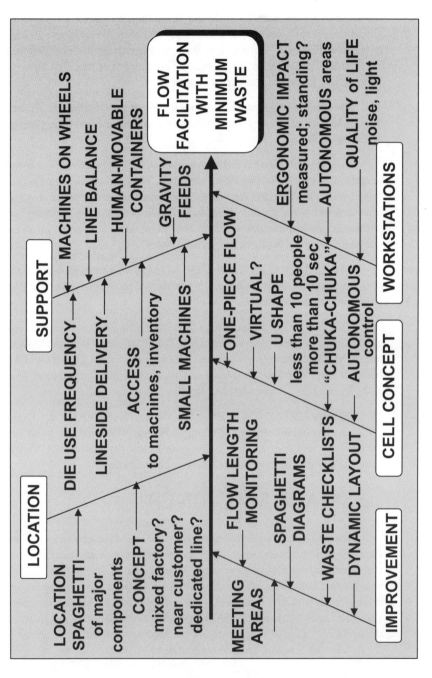

LOCATION

LOCATION
SPAGHETTI
of major
components

CONCEPT
mixed factory?
near customer?
dedicated line?

SUPPORT

DIE USE FREQUENCY
LINESIDE DELIVERY
ACCESS
to machines, inventory
SMALL MACHINES

MACHINES ON WHEELS
LINE BALANCE
HUMAN-MOVABLE
CONTAINERS
GRAVITY
FEEDS

**FLOW
FACILITATION
WITH
MINIMUM
WASTE**

IMPROVEMENT

MEETING
AREAS

FLOW LENGTH
MONITORING

SPAGHETTI
DIAGRAMS

WASTE CHECKLISTS

DYNAMIC LAYOUT

CELL CONCEPT

ONE-PIECE FLOW
VIRTUAL?
U SHAPE
less than 10 people
more than 10 sec
"CHUKA-CHUKA"
AUTONOMOUS
control

WORKSTATIONS

ERGONOMIC IMPACT
measured; standing?
AUTONOMOUS areas
QUALITY of LIFE
noise, light

34

The related sunk cost principle means that the priority should be with minimising present and future costs, not with keeping machines working to "pay off" a cost which has already been incurred. Therefore utilisation is irrelevant unless it is a capacity constrained machine.

In fact, maximising utilisation is counterproductive – something we learn from statistical thinking and from highway congestion where progress stalls when utilisation gets too high. The reduction in variation in machine cycles is as important as cycle time itself.

OLD MACHINES

The small machine concept can be extended to older machines. The best machine may well be an old machine that is quality capable, that is permanently set up, located just where needed, and that is written off in the books so that no-one cares about utilisation. It is throughput and lead-time that count. Beware of scrapping old machines that are still quality capable for machines that are faster.

SELF DEVELOPED MACHINES

Why should a machine be "at its worst when new"? Because it may not yet have had pokayoke devices fitted, may not yet be quality capable, may not yet have had low cost automation devices integrated with it, and may not yet have been developed for multiple operations. And especially if variation has not been tackled.

Developing machine capabilities "ahead of the game" is good policy. You may not have the time when you need it.

AUTOMATION

The prime reason for automation in lean is for quality. The principle is not to automate waste. So simplify first. Ask whether a low cost solution is possible – a gravity feed rather than a robot. Good reasons for automation are dull, dirty, dangerous and hot, heavy, hazardous. Another good reason is reduction in variation. A bad reason is to reduce people. Beware, machines don't make improvement suggestions.

LAYOUT

Layout sets the scene for Lean. Poor layout is perhaps the greatest ongoing source of waste and the greatest opportunity. Layout is a key facilitator because it makes small batch or one-piece-flow possible. By contrast, with non-lean layout there is no option but to move parts around in surging batches. Layout is also key to improved quality. So the overriding layout principle is to move machines and processes closer together, as soon as and whenever opportunities arise. (Opportunities always arise when buffer stock is reduced, when new machines are acquired, with new products, when changeover is reduced, and so on.) Traditional re-layout tended to take place only periodically; with lean, layout changes are made much more frequently.

Layout should be thought of as a hierarchical process – from plant location to factory layout, to cell layout, to workstation design.

LOCATION

Begin with a spaghetti diagram showing how major components get moved around before arriving at the plant and after they leave. Calculate the speed of this movement and ask searching questions on transport, location and batch sizes.

Plant concept reminds one to consider whether one should consider a mixed plant serving several customers, dedicated customer cells or lines on own site, a dedicated focused plant near a major customer, or moving onto a customer's site. The same considerations apply in reverse to your major suppliers.

SUPPORT

There are a whole raft of concepts which aid lean layout. Machines on wheels offers ultimate flexibility but may not be practical. Die use frequency reminds us to locate more frequently used dies closer to machines that use them. Do a Pareto. Lineside delivery by suppliers is the ideal, but a supermarket may be an interim solution. Cells and lines should be balanced against takt time, using actual times (no allowances). Cells or lines should not balanced to equalise work. Breaks are taken more frequently, and work is at standard rate or zero. (See Standards section). The shojinka concept alters the number of operators depending on takt time. This makes cross training necessary. Containers should be human-movable if possible, or parts moved by gravity feed. Machines require access, particularly around the back. Inventory footprints should be shown. The Small Machine concept (See separate section) is a major facilitator.

CELL CONCEPT

The fundamental advantage of cells is one-piece flow. (The reason is reduction in lead-time. This is Little's Law: Throughput = batch size / lead-time, so for a constant throughput, lead-time is directly proportional to batch size.) If flow is not one-piece you do not have a lean cell! Inventory standards should exist in every cell. A lean ideal is frequently U shape with operators within arms length. There may be a series of U cells. Cycle times less than about 10 seconds are undesirable for checking and improvement reasons. More than about 10 people in a cell prevents full cross training flexibility and works against the team concept. A variation is the chuka chuka line that slowly moves a wheeled pallet past a workstation in the takt time. Another is the virtual cell that is used if machines are too large to locate into a physical cell. Here operators from several sequential processes work as a team rather than for their own process department. Simplicity of control and reduced leadtime frequently more than compensate for any capacity loss. Cells should be autonomous with integrated quality, maintenance, and sometimes schedule responsibility.

WORKSTATIONS

Workstations need to be designed with their ergonomic impact and the waste of motion in mind. Minimise both horizontal movement and vertical movement of parts and tools. Standing may be better than sitting for flexibility and posture. Autonomous layout means full responsibility in designated areas. Quality of life should be improved by considering noise, light, floors, of course safety.

IMPROVEMENT

Begins by knowing flowlengths and trying to minimise. Spaghetti diagrams are powerful aids and factory and workstation level. Waste checklists, prepared by lean promotion office, help keep muda in mind. Meeting areas, in which performance is displayed, is great for teamwork and improvement. A flip chart to note problems immediately should be an essential item in every cell.

5S

5S is the basic housekeeping discipline for lean, quality and safety. It applies in office and on shop floor equally. Everyone has the experience of working better and feeling better in a tidy room. But it's also a mindset thing – changing attitudes from "I work in a dirty factory" to "I work in a manufacturing laboratory".

SORT

The first step is to CLASSIFY literally everything by frequency. A good idea to do this with the team and to touch everything systematically. If used every day, is the quantity correct? If used weekly can it be brought

Lean and 5S

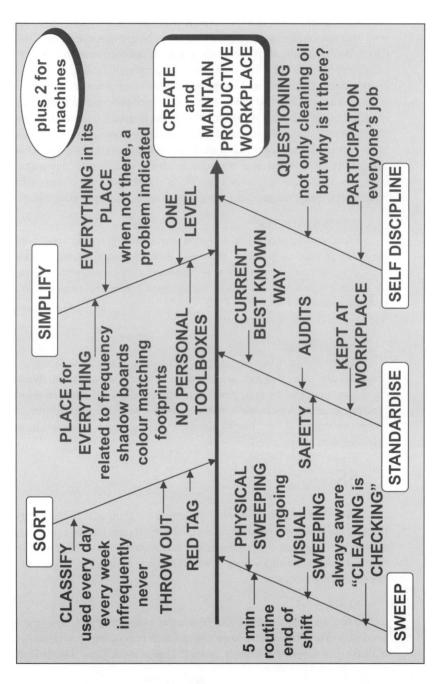

out weekly? If used monthly should it rather be located in the store? If never, or in doubt, then red tag or throw out. A Red Tag is a label with the date; if no one accesses it within a specified period it should be thrown out.

SIMPLIFY
A place for everything (using shadowboards, inventory footprints, tools and dies on trolleys or at the right height, and colour matching to link associated tools). And everything in its place (if not there and not in use, a problem is indicated). Personal toolboxes are discouraged because you want the tools for the job at the job in standardised locations for operator flexibility. The standard is The "Dental Surgery". Why? Because all can relate to that standard of excellence. "One level" means trying to keep dies, tools and parts at the same level as the workplace to minimise bending.

These first two steps need to be repeated periodically.

SWEEP
This includes physical tidy up, on an ongoing basis, and·"visual sweeping" whereby operators are always on the lookout for anything out of place, and try to correct it immediately. Some companies adopt a 5 minute routine whereby operators work out a 5 minute cleanup routine for each day of the week such that by week end everything has been covered the required number of times.

"Cleaning is Checking" means that these are integrated. You don't just clean up, you check for any abnormality and its root causes.

STANDARDISE
Housekeeping standards need to be maintained. See the section on standards. Carry out audits on housekeeping regularly. Some award a floating trophy for achievement.

SELF DISCIPLINE
Everyone participates in 5S on an ongoing basis. Self-discipline is about participation and improvement. Not just cleaning up the oil but asking why it is there in the first place.

Note: Alternatives for 5S (but basically the same thing) are Simplify, Straighten, Scrub, Stabilise, Sustain or CANDO – Cleanup, Arrange, Neatness, Discipline, Ongoing improvement

Lean and CHANGEOVER REDUCTION

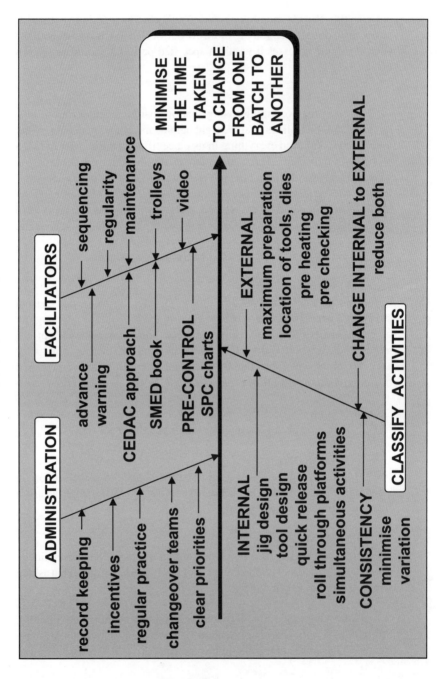

MINIMISE THE TIME TAKEN TO CHANGE FROM ONE BATCH TO ANOTHER

ADMINISTRATION
- record keeping
- incentives
- regular practice
- changeover teams
- clear priorities

FACILITATORS
- advance warning
- sequencing
- regularity
- CEDAC approach
- maintenance
- SMED book
- trolleys
- PRE-CONTROL SPC charts
- video

INTERNAL
- jig design
- tool design
- quick release
- roll through platforms
- simultaneous activities

CONSISTENCY
- minimise variation

CLASSIFY ACTIVITIES

EXTERNAL
- maximum preparation
- location of tools, dies
- pre heating
- pre checking

CHANGE INTERNAL to EXTERNAL
- reduce both

TWO EXTRA FOR MACHINES.

The 7 steps of Autonomous Maintenance are very similar to 5S except that there are two additions (1) implementing countermeasures to defects (pokayoke and others) and sources of contamination and (2) autonomous internal checking, not just external as in 5S. The first of these follows the sort or cleanup stage and the second is done after external simplification.

CHANGEOVER REDUCTION

The prime reasons for changeover reduction in lean is for flexibility and reduced batch sizes, leading to lead time competitivess. Improved changeover also, surprisingly, leads to improved quality through consistent repetition. A less good reason is to increase capacity, especially if it leads to overproduction.

Note that changeover is defined as the time from the last piece of one batch to the first good piece of the next batch. In some cases the limitation on batch sizes is not the internal changeover time (when the machine is stopped) but the external time for changeover preparation. So both need to be reduced as well as the time for adjustment and inspection.

Note also that changeover reduction is not limited to machine changeover. Line changeover, vehicle load and unload, maintenance operations, and many office operations are also relevant.

- Consistency is a big issue. It is not much good having a changeover that sometimes takes 10 minutes but sometimes takes 30 minutes. Sometimes, to achieve schedule adherence, it is more important to be consistent than quick but variable. Standardisation should certainly be a goal.

The classic analogy is with a grand prix pit stop. The same principles apply.

CLASSIFY ACTIVITIES

Shingo's classic single-minute exchange of die (SMED) approach is to flowchart the changeover and to classify into internal and external activities. See if any internal activities can be done externally. External: Do the maximum amount of preparation before the machine is stopped. This includes locating tools and dies on trolleys, colour coding to avoid confusion, locating frequently used dies nearer to machines, pre-heating and pre-checking (and post changeover checking also to maximise the time available). Internal: many internal improvements involve the use of simple though sometimes sophisticated devices – quick release nuts, standard die heights, roll through platforms, jig and tool design, use of hydraulic and electric aids. Remember the quality side – incorporate failsafing devices, off line checks, and testing procedures (sometimes it is sampling that takes the longest time).

The process should be mapped and the "critical path" determined. A spaghetti diagram of operator movements is useful.

FACILITATORS

Correct sequencing of changeovers, from major to minor, from dark colour to light may help. So may regularity where a changeover takes place at approximately the same time each day or week. (Dies are always ready, so is the forklift, so are the parts to be processed, etc.). Preventive maintenance of tools, dies, and machines is essential to retain changeover consistency. Trolleys on which is placed, by shadowboard and colour coded, all necessary tools and dies, preferably at the correct height, are useful. Every changeover should be videoed with time lapse camera.

Advance warning means having a clear signal (lights, audio) when a changeover is due to warn the changeover team and the forklift driver. Cause and Effect diagrams with addition of cards (CEDAC) diagrams to record past achievements and tasks still to be done. Shingo's SMED book is the bible on changeover. And pre-control SPC charts are a good way to get quickly onto defect prevention.

ADMINISTRATION

An aspect frequently ignored is to chart every changeover time on a run diagram. This helps encourage consistency and to trace sources of problems. Team members should feel free to write ideas and memos on the chart – use rather than appearance is preferred. Incentives are both financial and non-financial. Although output incentives are not compatible with lean, consistency and achievement may well be rewarded. Non-financial reward and recognition is necessary to retain good performance. As in a grand prix team, practise makes perfect; you don't have to make parts to practise and perfect a changeover. Teams, as in a grand prix should do critical changeovers. And changeovers should enjoy clear priority over all (?) support activities; never delay a changeover by a non-customer critical activity.

TEAM PREPARATION

Some lean progress can be made without involving teams, but will soon plateau. Lean is team process. It requires new attitudes and practices by managers and operators. Trust on both sides has to be built over time. The aim is to create thinking, participating, stakeholders not mere employees.

POLICY

A basic concept is to "hire the whole person" – his or her skills, brain, all the senses, and all the potential. Aim to hire people who are willing to contribute in this full way. Most will need to be team players. Participation has to become the norm – progress displays, newsletters, and team briefings all help. Line and staff equality, on benefits, facilities, conditions of employment, and even parking fosters teamwork and communication, creates job security, and "drives out fear". Participation cannot include people improving themselves out of a job. But no company can guarantee ultimate job security, so everyone must understand the difference between the risks of the market and the security of making improvements. Training for lifetime skills is the ultimate job security for today's insecure market place. A company may not be able to guarantee job security but can help operators to build their marketability so benefit both company and themselves. Annualised hours helps with non-stable demand by calling in work as needed but guaranteeing minimum and maximum monthly and annual number of hours. A win for both company and operator. Fewer job categories leads to greater flexibility and improved security. The right attitude is more important than the right skills, many of which can be added later.

Capacity through people is the belief that capacity can be increased not only by extra machines and space, but also through people having greater and more flexible skills. Developing people is often more cost effective than buying physical plant.

REWARDS AND INCENTIVES

Rewards and incentives must not compromise quality; overproduction or any other wastes but should encourage improvement. Gainsharing, with benefits shared on the basis of improvements, seems to be compatible with lean. But the big one is recognition – always thanks, sometimes celebrations and recognition boards.

Lean and TEAM PREPARATION

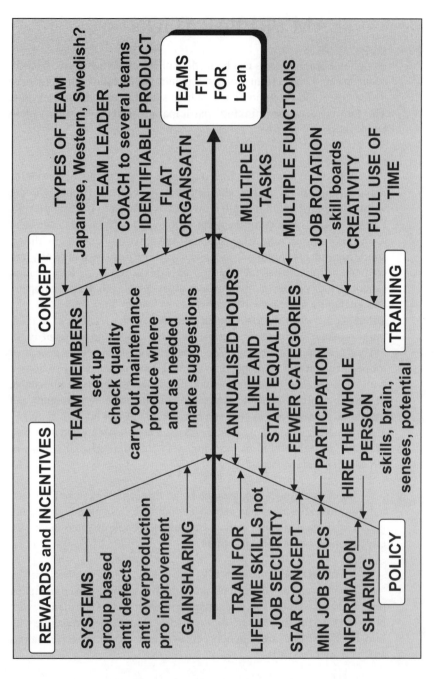

TEAMS FIT FOR Lean

CONCEPT

TYPES OF TEAM
Japanese, Western, Swedish?
TEAM LEADER
COACH to several teams
IDENTIFIABLE PRODUCT
FLAT
ORGANSATN

TEAM MEMBERS
set up
check quality
carry out maintenance
produce where
and as needed
make suggestions

TRAINING

MULTIPLE
TASKS
MULTIPLE FUNCTIONS
JOB ROTATION
skill boards
CREATIVITY
FULL USE OF
TIME

REWARDS and INCENTIVES

SYSTEMS
group based
anti defects
anti overproduction
pro improvement
GAINSHARING

ANNUALISED HOURS
LINE AND
STAFF EQUALITY
FEWER CATEGORIES
PARTICIPATION
HIRE THE WHOLE
PERSON
skills, brain,
senses, potential

TRAIN FOR
LIFETIME SKILLS not
JOB SECURITY
STAR CONCEPT
MIN JOB SPECS
INFORMATION
SHARING

POLICY

Incentive schemes need to reward the quantity of suggestions, not just the quality. The Pareto principle applies – a few good suggestions make a whole incentive scheme worthwhile, but to get to those few many need to be sifted through.

CONCEPT

The team concept is one of the most important developments accompanying lean. It begins with operators that are multi-functional. This leads to quality of worklife – involvement, participation, security, and growth, even perhaps fun.

Edward Lawler's "Star" concept (People, Strategy, Structure, Processes, Rewards) is a useful checklist on areas that must be considered whilst setting up a team.

Teams evolve into self-direction, where team leaders are elected by and responsible to, the team not the company. At the same time former supervisors become coaches who decide with, rather than for, teams. (Coaches are chosen by, and responsible to, management.)

Note that there are three approaches to teams. The Japanese approach uses teams for improvement and the team may have responsibility for line balance, but the supervisor has authority for work allocation and team wellbeing. Here there may be quality circles – voluntary but permanent. Toyota also uses several other types of team, which are appointed for a specific purpose and disbanded at the end of the study. The Western approach goes further with self-direction. Here the team eventually assumes responsibility for many activities – with team leadership rotating depending upon the problem. The third approach is the "Swedish" model where teams build whole products or assemblies with very long cycle times. This approach has been abandoned by its originator, Volvo, but remains useful for some specialised tasks.

TRAINING

Skills should be displayed on a team matrix board using a U or other symbol that is filled in as team members progress from beginner to teacher. Training should include not only job skills, but also problem solving and teamworking skills.

Education and training should take place "just in time" linking theory with immediate practice. There is a cycle to identify the next skill, train for it, test, and consolidate before moving onto the next skill.

Lean and TEAM INVOLVEMENT

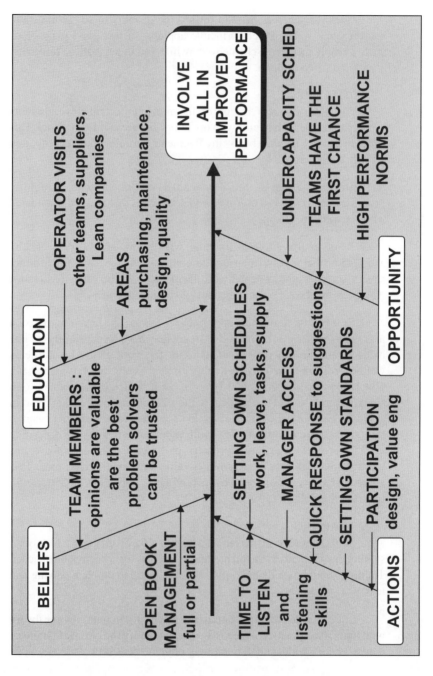

BELIEFS

EDUCATION

TEAM MEMBERS : opinions are valuable are the best problem solvers can be trusted

OPEN BOOK MANAGEMENT full or partial

OPERATOR VISITS other teams, suppliers, Lean companies

AREAS purchasing, maintenance, design, quality

INVOLVE ALL IN IMPROVED PERFORMANCE

SETTING OWN SCHEDULES work, leave, tasks, supply

MANAGER ACCESS

QUICK RESPONSE to suggestions

SETTING OWN STANDARDS

PARTICIPATION design, value eng

TIME TO LISTEN and listening skills

UNDERCAPACITY SCHED

TEAMS HAVE THE FIRST CHANCE

HIGH PERFORMANCE NORMS

OPPORTUNITY

ACTIONS

Stage 2

TEAM INVOLVEMENT

Team Involvement builds on Team Preparation and aims to involve all in achieving improved performance.

BELIEFS

The underlying belief is that those close to the action are best qualified to make improvements, they are good problem solvers (at least with coaching) and can be trusted to lead the attack on waste. This implies a new role for "experts" such as industrial engineers, maintenance engineers, and quality professionals who become facilitators and coaches rather than front line improvers. The experts need to be good listeners because operators have valuable opinions.

ACTIONS

Increasingly self directed teams are taking over tasks such as scheduling, work allocation, leave, hiring, purchasing, even rewards. Teams can communicate horizontally whilst notifying management ("U") rather than having to work up and down the organisational hierarchy ("H"). Shopfloor team members are also useful in design and value engineering studies, so as to improve manufacturability.

It usually takes two years for a team to evolve into full self-directed status, and in the early years there may well be a drop in productivity as the team finds its feet. But in many companies the rewards of self-direction are great: improved quality and productivity, reduced staff turnover, increased flexibility – in short a flatter and leaner organisation.

Open Book Management is a growing concept whereby information on both the "financials" and operations is given to operators, in whole or in part, to help them make better suggestions. It is also about involvement, belief, and trust.

OPPORTUNITY

Teams must have the first chance to make improvements themselves, before "experts" step in. This fosters ownership. Undercapacity scheduling

Lean and VISIBILITY

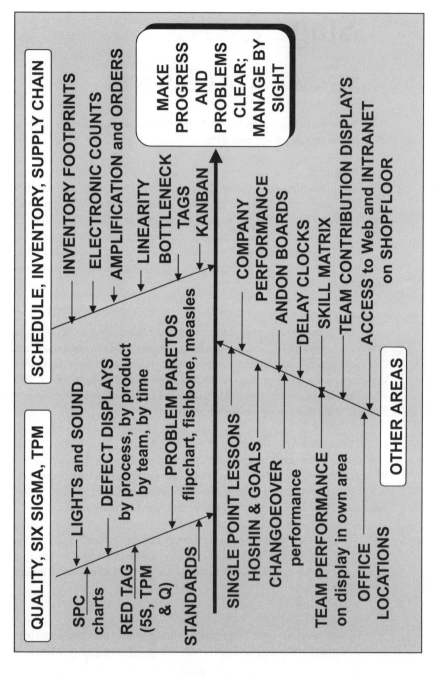

QUALITY, SIX SIGMA, TPM

SPC charts

LIGHTS and SOUND

RED TAG (5S, TPM & Q)

DEFECT DISPLAYS
by process, by product
by team, by time

STANDARDS

PROBLEM PARETOS
flipchart, fishbone, measles

SCHEDULE, INVENTORY, SUPPLY CHAIN

INVENTORY FOOTPRINTS

ELECTRONIC COUNTS

AMPLIFICATION and ORDERS

LINEARITY

BOTTLENECK TAGS

KANBAN

MAKE PROGRESS AND PROBLEMS CLEAR; MANAGE BY SIGHT

SINGLE POINT LESSONS

HOSHIN & GOALS

CHANGEOVER performance

TEAM PERFORMANCE on display in own area

OFFICE LOCATIONS

COMPANY PERFORMANCE

ANDON BOARDS

DELAY CLOCKS

SKILL MATRIX

TEAM CONTRIBUTION DISPLAYS

ACCESS to Web and INTRANET on SHOPFLOOR

OTHER AREAS

deliberately allows time for improvement, and offsets the squeezing out of thinking by output pressure. All this should work in an atmosphere of high performance norms, where teams are expected to perform well and to improve. Expectation breeds results – the "Pygmalion" effect is proven.

EDUCATION

Team members should assist in educating both themselves and other members. Visits to other teams, good lean companies, and to suppliers and customers builds understanding and motivation and helps cut waste. Education should be "just in time" – application immediately following instruction.

VISIBILITY

Visibility is a major principle in Lean. If you are guided by the maxim of managing by sight you will not go far wrong. Visibility means a change in management style; from managing by remote control to managing by walking about. Visibility also implies simplicity – a workplace where anything out of order is immediately seen. For the Supply Chain, visibility means transparency of information upstream and downstream. Sharing demand, quality, customer, and design information upstream and downstream.

QUALITY, SIX SIGMA AND TPM

Standards and standard operating procedures (SOPs) belong at the workplace, not in the office. Photos and sketches should support them. The red tag concept is a way of drawing attention to activities needing attention. In TPM red tags show jobs outstanding. In 5S tags show items that may be thrown out. In suggestion schemes tags show ideas requiring a response. Lights and sound also draw attention to activities requiring attention. At Toyota tunes are played when machines breakdown; each machine has its own tune. SPC charts and other variation performance should be kept at the process. Likewise all forms of defect displays. Two-dimensional checklists, for instance showing operators on one-axis and defect types on the other give multi-dimensional information. Alternative axes may be time, product, process. A flipchart should be kept at every cell. Measles charts can be kept for products, for accident near misses, for suggestions, for stoppages and other possibilities. All build up into automatic Pareto charts. Fishbone diagrams can be used to summarise, as in this book.

SCHEDULE, INVENTORY AND SUPPLY CHAIN

Inventory footprints allow any operator or passing manager to see at a glance the inventory status. Any stillage out of place is immediately seen. Electronic counts keep an automatic check on schedule progress or press strokes and display these against a running target. Managers in charge of schedules should insist upon seeing graphics of "variation and amplification" (see the final figure on basic mapping tools). This gives real motivation to schedulers and supervisors to work to plan. It is also powerful in supply chain. Linearity tracks progress against schedule and measures the amount of variation. Also a motivator. Bottleneck tags show jobs that need to be progressed onto or after a bottleneck operation. And of course kanban boards and cards, including heijunka boards, are a powerful visual way to keep track of schedule progress.

OTHER AREAS

Hoshin Goals (the few critical goals to be achieved) should be clearly and prominently displayed. And how the company is performing against the targets should be on display.

Graphing changeover times gives good incentive to retain consistency.

Each team should maintain a set of statistics and graphs relating to their own performance. Better to let teams do this themselves than to have "professional" graphs plotted on a central computer. A skill matrix, showing progress from beginner to master in each skill category belongs in team areas. Names are shown on one axis and skills on the other axis. The contribution of team members to improvement is best shown at or near the workplace.

Delay clocks keep an ongoing accumulated record of time lost on the line or in a cell through stoppage. Everyone thereby knows the liklihood of having to work extra time. Moreover the record helps pinpoint problem areas. Overhead Andon boards display stoppage information which can be seen over a long distance, which encourages quick response from supervisors, maintenance or quality. Such stoppages may be linked to a computer system that builds up a Pareto of accumulated problems.

Locating offices so that their occupants can be accessible and be seen is good policy. A trick is to locate design offices so that designers must cross the shop floor to get there. Common refreshment areas serve similar purposes.

Some companies (e.g. Ford) give access to the Ford intranet from the shopfloor. This opens up huge information possibilities.

PROCESS DATA COLLECTION

Process Data Collection is the principle of collecting and making use of data at the process or workplace. Much process data collection involves the use of electronic devices, but manual operations are also effective. This principle needs to be thought of as a partner of the Visibility principle. It assists the philosophy of Gemba – going to the workplace and collecting the facts.

INVENTORY and SCHEDULING

Bar codes avoid identification errors and assist with replacement stock records and kanban calls. Linearity tracking involves a line-side display of the planned production schedule that is kept up-to-date on an hourly basis. Cell leaders are able to see the accumulated backlog of work at any time and can make early decisions on extra work required to hit the schedule target. Delay clocks automatically accumulate lost time on an assembly line and allow real-time schedule updating and decision-making Automatic counting of parts made or production cycles gives an on-going measure performance and relieves operators of the need to count. Re-keying is eliminated, and so too is delay and error. In the supply chain use of the web and EDI allow instant communication from the point of demand. Pressure sensors indicate when a pallet or storage space is not in use, interfacing with inventory systems.

MES (Manufacturing Execution System) terminals link directly into e business systems to communicate with suppliers and customers. Beware however of MES links with MRP or ERP scheduling which can move you back to centralised complexity (the old way) rather than decentralised simplicity.

MACHINES

Automatic condition monitoring (e.g. of temperature, vibration, dimensions) gives an early warning of problems. Pokayoke devices can be included for this purpose. Red tags are hung on lineside boards to indicate maintenance requirements and backlogs. Run hour recording gives automatic data on OEE factors (run/idle/changeover/speed/breakdown) providing powerful maintenance information. Status displays automatically indicate progress such as parts made, press strokes, and tool status. The last two can be interfaced with maintenance to automatically indicate maintenance or tool change requirements.

Lean and PROCESS DATA COLLECTION

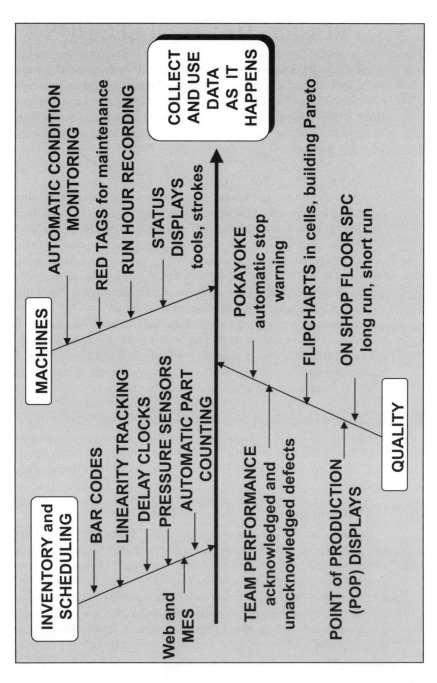

52

QUALITY

SPC is a well-established area of process data collection with charts being plotted automatically or by operators. Interpretation of charts for out-of-control or developing problems belongs at the workplace. Short-run SPC is a developing area for small batch production. Pokayoke (error proofing) devices incorporate either stop or warning, and carry out 100% automatic inspection. Immediate action is demanded. Teams need to be encouraged to take responsibility for quality in a "no fears" climate. One way is line-stop but another, where defects are made or noticed but which cannot be immediately rectified, is for operators to place stickers on the part to identify the problem. Accumulations are monitored.

Point of Production (POP) control devices cover a wide variety of decision aids which may incorporate artificial intelligence to help interpret quality or control in process, chemical and electronic industries. Remote automatic sensing is a growing area.

Perhaps the most simple but effective process data collection device is the flipchart which is kept at the cell and on which all problems are noted, and recurrences recorded, so as to accumulate into a Pareto chart.

IMPROVEMENT

Improvement is the lean way of life. And rapid improvement can only be achieved through full participation. At the heart of Lean improvement lie four basics: first, make everyone continuously aware of the 7 wastes, based on those suggested by Taiichi Ohno. These are shown on a separate figure. Dan Jones encourages people to "wear their Muda spectacles". Second, encourage everyone to have a questioning attitude and to use the five whys. Third is Kaizen, which is a belief in on-going improvements, made project by project by teams and consolidated, rather than a few big improvements made by "experts". Kaizen is complementary to break through improvements such as Kaizen Blitz. Fourth, is continuous improvement through one improvement leading to another leading to another. This can be thought of as the Stage 1 concepts leading to the stage 2 concepts that in turn lead back to Stage 1.

MAPPING

Mapping is the way to direct improvements rather than leaping in in a haphazard fashion. "Learning to See" or big picture mapping is a high-level mapping tool to identify problems and opportunities from supplier to

Lean and IMPROVEMENT

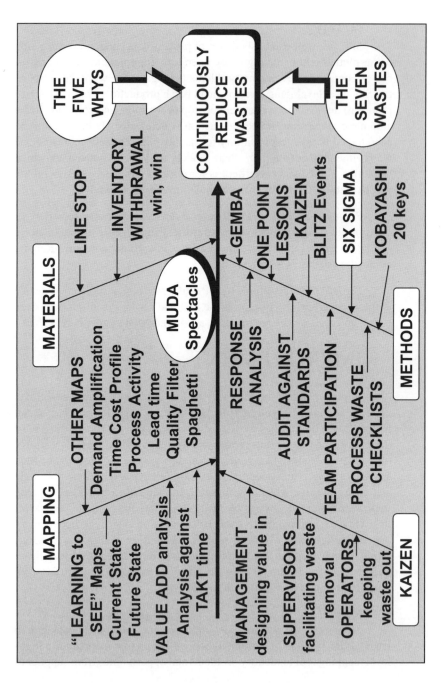

THE FIVE WHYS

THE SEVEN WASTES

CONTINUOUSLY REDUCE WASTES

MATERIALS

LINE STOP

INVENTORY WITHDRAWAL
win, win

MAPPING

OTHER MAPS
Demand Amplification
Time Cost Profile
Process Activity
Lead time
Quality Filter
Spaghetti

MUDA Spectacles

"LEARNING to SEE" Maps
Current State
Future State

VALUE ADD analysis
Analysis against TAKT time

GEMBA
ONE POINT LESSONS
KAIZEN
BLITZ Events

SIX SIGMA

KOBAYASHI
20 keys

METHODS

RESPONSE ANALYSIS

AUDIT AGAINST STANDARDS

TEAM PARTICIPATION

PROCESS WASTE CHECKLISTS

MANAGEMENT designing value in

SUPERVISORS facilitating waste removal

OPERATORS keeping waste out

KAIZEN

THE SEVEN WASTES
after Taiichi Ohno

OVERPRODUCING — too early, too much, just-in-case

WAITING — materials queuing, not moving / people not productively employed / expediting

TRANSPORTING — all materials movement, double handling

INAPPROPRIATE PROCESSING — too fast, too big, too variable / one big machine instead of several smaller

UNNECESSARY INVENTORY — stores, buffers, batch sizes / and their control systems

UNNECESSARY MOTIONS — reaching, bending, exertion, excess walking / excessive turns to loosen, unpack

DEFECTS — rework, rejects, unnecessary inspection; / consequences of not doing it right the first time

customer. How the current state is to be transformed into the future state is directed by a series of questions relating to takt time, bottlenecks, location of buffers and supermarkets, and the possibilities of flow and pull. Normally, both short-term and long-term opportunities are identified. Value add analysis determines the proportions of time and activities that are value adding, non value adding, and temporary but necessary non value adding.

Other maps. Demand amplification maps track actual performance of orders and batches at each stage of manufacturing against time. The amplification of orders and the consistency of the schedule can be tracked. Time cost profiles track the cost build up of value adding and non-value adding activity against time. Plateaus indicate areas of inactivity, and the divergence of the two lines indicates the build up of waste. Process activity maps are the traditional industrial engineering tools of detailed activity analysis, classifying each activity into operation, delay, inspect, etc and are used to home in on areas of special concern. The lead time map identifies how lead-time is broken down. It will frequently be the case that most time is used off the factory floor. The spaghetti diagram traces the physical movement of parts.

MATERIALS

Improvement in the materials area is encouraged by line stop that gives operators the authority to stop production when quality, shortage, or maintenance problems arise. Line stop must be accompanied by a signalling device to demand appropriate response, and by a "no fear " attitude. Line stoppage must attempt to seek the root cause, not merely arrange a temporary fix. Deliberate inventory withdrawal encourages improvement by seeking to expose the next most limiting factor. The concept is that inventory covers up unseen problems. Remove some inventory and experiment! Identify the problem thus exposed and work on it. Inventory is usually withdrawn by removing a kanban card or by cutting a kanban quantity - supervisors or teams should suggest where cuts could be attempted. This is a "win win" strategy; either inventory is reduced or waste is identified. This is one way to continue with lean implementation: begin "loose" and gradually tighten. However, a safer approach (for lean beginners) is to identify problems first (say by mapping), remove problems, and then reduce inventory.

METHODS

A basic approach is to "go to gemba" and collect the facts. Standards are the building block for continuous improvement. Standards should be audited and deviations identified. The idea is not to be a policeman but to build on best-known and safest way. Response analysis also highlights problem areas. Here the time to respond to line stop or maintenance or quality problems is monitored. Process waste checklists are prepared by the lean promotion office and issued to everyone including office workers. These lists contain questions such as "do you walk to pick up parts?" If yes, there is waste and you are challenged on how to reduce it. Another form of audit is the Kobayashi 20 key questionnaire that identifies the areas of strength and weakness and provokes improvement ideas.

Kaizen Blitz events aim to attack wastes in specific cells or small areas during a 3 or five-day full-time all-out attack on waste. These events include operators, managers, and outside staff and experts. The idea is to "just do it" without delay. Improvement rather than perfection is the aim. Analyse, implement, test, and standardise are all done within a week.

Six Sigma (see separate section) is a major alternative focusing on the reduction of variation and improvement.

MASTER SCHEDULING

Scheduling is at the heart of Lean, and good master scheduling is the foundation. Lean aims to make at customer rates of demand. However, despite demand management (see separate section) demand rates often vary throughout the year.

STABILITY
Stability is created for each period by planning for regular, stable rate plateaus that smooth out the demand peaks and troughs. Plateaus will be established according to forecasted demand and only altered if "control limits" are breached. This is similar to SPC. Engineering changes are grouped and brought together when the schedule rate changes, an exception being safety-critical changes. In made-to-order, time fences are established within which the schedule remains frozen.

DEVELOPMENT
The schedule is developed with the underlying principle of making, as far as possible, some of each product every day (if not every day, every second day, and so on). The regularity principle is a guide. Try to make the same product on the same day each week, perhaps in different batch quantities. Even better, try to make every product every day. This approach

Lean and MASTER SCHEDULING

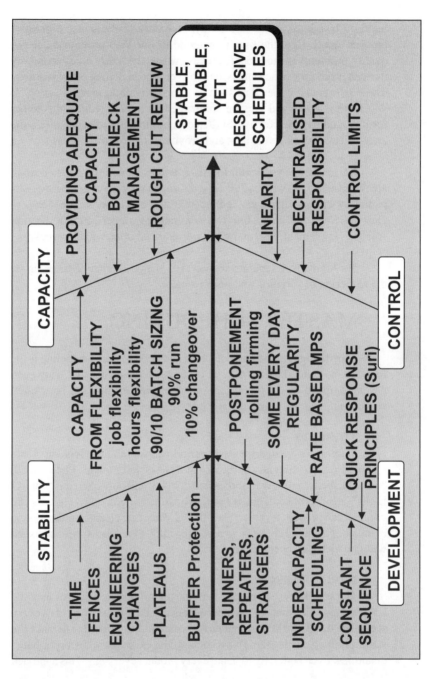

STABLE, ATTAINABLE, YET RESPONSIVE SCHEDULES

STABILITY

TIME FENCES

ENGINEERING CHANGES

PLATEAUS

BUFFER Protection

CAPACITY

CAPACITY FROM FLEXIBILITY
job flexibility
hours flexibility

90/10 BATCH SIZING
90% run
10% changeover

PROVIDING ADEQUATE CAPACITY

BOTTLENECK MANAGEMENT

ROUGH CUT REVIEW

DEVELOPMENT

RUNNERS, REPEATERS, STRANGERS

POSTPONEMENT
rolling firming

SOME EVERY DAY REGULARITY

RATE BASED MPS

UNDERCAPACITY SCHEDULING

CONSTANT SEQUENCE

QUICK RESPONSE PRINCIPLES (Suri)

CONTROL

LINEARITY

DECENTRALISED RESPONSIBILITY

CONTROL LIMITS

has implications for the entire plant, its layout, its people, and its machines. Scheduling 500 units once per quarter produces about same output as one unit per hour or eight per day, but the implications of very different. So beware of "batch and queue" mentality. Schedules should be rate based (i.e. so many per day) rather than work order based. First classify the product line into runners, repeaters, and strangers. Runners get their own dedicated facilities or cells. Repeaters (items with regular demand) should be fitted into regular slots in the schedule (for example make product XYZ every Tuesday). Strangers are fitted in around the repeaters. (By the way, we run our lives on this basis with the heart being a runner, fairly regular sleep or meals being the repeaters, and other activities being strangers.)

Under capacity scheduling means planning to less than the full time available per day or per week. This permits 100 per cent schedule achievement by allowing a time buffer for a certain proportion of disruption. It also allows time for decision-making on quality. If events work perfectly the time is devoted to improvement activities or housekeeping. This recognises variation, is central idea in statistical thinking.

Postponement means developing schedules which attempt to maintain variety as long as possible. This will usually require design or process adjustments, but scheduling has a role to play also. A rolling schedule is a possibility. As time progresses, schedules are firmed, moving from liquid to slushy to frozen.

Quick response principles (Rajan Suri) concentrate on flow and time by preventing parts from being launched before has available capacity - like not authorising an airline flight before landing clearance is obtained. This is a variation on Goldratt's Drum-Buffer-Rope principle.

CAPACITY

A master schedule must be valid from a capacity standpoint. The Lean approach is to provide adequate capacity (i.e. lead capacity rather than lag capacity) to give flexibility. This can be aided by flexible labour working contracts. If there are constrained resources or bottlenecks, construct a schedule by forward scheduling on bottlenecks, whilst pulling through on the rest. Theory of constraints specifies that buffers be kept in front of bottlenecks and its subsequent assembly operations, but nowhere else. APS may help planning, but not execution that should be run by visibility. But beware of a return to job shop mentality rather than lean

Lean and INVENTORY

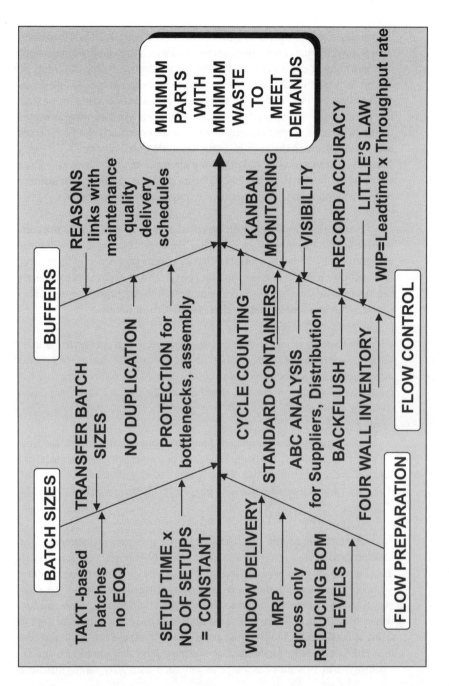

MINIMUM
PARTS
WITH
MINIMUM
WASTE
TO
MEET
DEMANDS

BATCH SIZES

TRANSFER BATCH SIZES

NO DUPLICATION

PROTECTION for bottlenecks, assembly

TAKT-based batches
no EOQ

SETUP TIME x
NO OF SETUPS
= CONSTANT

BUFFERS

REASONS
links with
maintenance
quality
delivery
schedules

FLOW PREPARATION

WINDOW DELIVERY

MRP
gross only
REDUCING BOM
LEVELS

CYCLE COUNTING

STANDARD CONTAINERS

ABC ANALYSIS
for Suppliers, Distribution

BACKFLUSH

FOUR WALL INVENTORY

FLOW CONTROL

KANBAN

MONITORING

VISIBILITY

RECORD ACCURACY

LITTLE'S LAW
WIP=Leadtime x Throughput rate

60

regularity and simplicity. Rough-cut capacity evaluation will be needed at times of rate change, but keep the evaluation simple; a spreadsheet rather than APS will often suffice.

In some operations batching is inevitable. The Toyota press-shop approach is to fix the overall ratio between run time and changeover at 90/10. (It turns out that this is often a near-optimal policy). This governs batch sizes and campaign length but also prevents changeover times from slipping.

CONTROL
Linearity should be the aim of schedule attainment. Here, a regular flow of work throughout the day is planned and displayed and deviations measured. Responsibility for schedule execution and detailed scheduling should be devolved to cells. A key for simplicity and attainment. Control limits prevent over-reaction to demand changes – "tinkering" with schedules is as destructive as tinkering with machine adjustment.

INVENTORY

Lean is not all about inventory reduction. But inventory reduction helps to move you towards lean by exposing problems, reducing lead-time, improving visibility and responsiveness to quality problems, and by reducing flow length. In fact, good inventory performance is the RESULT of other lean activities. Reducing inventory arbitrarily is often counterproductive.

BATCH SIZE
A key for flexibility is batch size reduction. It helps to establish a link with changeover time. As changeover time is reduced, the number of changeovers should increase so their product remains a constant. If changeover time is halved, number of changeovers should double and batch size should halve. Note that this does not correspond with EOQ thinking! Don't use the EOQ – batch sizes should be related to takt time with the sum of changeover times plus run times in line with overall demand.

Inter-process transfer batch sizes should be kept as small as possible compatible with (human-movable?) material handling – so as to maximise overlap and flow.

BUFFERS
Buffers protect against uncertainty, but over-protection should be avoided. As in main stores and sub stores. As after the last process and in

front of the next one. As in protecting for both delivery and quality uncertainties when the likelihood of both together is small. Avoid duplication.

Awareness of the reasons for buffers – maintenance, quality, supply variability, lead times – should lead to immediate cuts in buffers when reasons are removed through improvement efforts. The schedule accuracy feedback loop works like this: Cutting lead times (as a result of various lean activities) improves schedule adherence. With improved adherence buffers can be cut. And cutting buffers leads to a cut in lead-time. And so on. But for finished goods the situation may be different: with many smaller batch sizes instead of a fewer larger batches, there will be more occasions during which there is a risk of stock-out. This means that it may be necessary to increase safety stocks – but remember that lead times are down so this should compensate. And overall WIP levels will be sharply down. As Lean progresses it may be possible to convert make-to-stock operations to make to order, resulting in better service with lower inventory.

FLOW CONTROL

Little's law is fundamental. WIP = lead-time x throughput rate. So there are two routes to reduce WIP. But also throughput cannot be increased without either increasing WIP or reducing lead-time (This is sometimes forgotten!).

Record accuracy and bill of material accuracy is also fundamental. The former can be improved by cycle counting, counting a few parts each day and tracking sources of error. Standardised containers or "eggcrates" containing specific numbers of parts making counting easier. And visibility is improved by kanban. For supply and distribution inventories, ABC (80/20) analysis is highly cost effective – paying particular attention to A category parts, and simply having C parts. In manufacture, A parts are brought to the line under kanban control, C parts are replenished by two bin methods. Throughout, all storage locations should be designed on the visibility and footprinting principle – making deviations immediately apparent. SPC principles can be used to control and improve record accuracy and to monitor supply lead times. Monitor delivery performance on time; quantity, and quality – failure on any one represents overall failure.

Tracking inventory is waste, particularly when fast moving. So record it only when it enters and leaves – the "four wall" system. With low defect levels, backflushing becomes possible – moving from subassembly backflushing to product level superflush. Flushing updates inventory records by deducting all parts that are assumed to have been used. Backflushing also gives a check on bill of material accuracy.

Kanban monitoring keeps visible track of backlogs by the number of cards on the board. Externally, kanban monitoring helps keep track of the sequence of arrival and departure of cards.

FLOW PREPARATION

Flow preparation begins with good accuracy, as above. MRP may be required but only for planning purposes, not execution. Gross-only MRP (no netting) may suffice at well developed lean sites. Reducing bill of material levels does away with unnecessary complexity. Single level bills are the norm in cellular manufacturing. BOMs should be restructured in line with changes in layout. Window deliveries, targeted at specific times, extend flow preparation to the supply chain.

Note: MRP does not work for shop floor execution because it makes the fatal error of not recognising variation.

PULL AND SYNCHRONISATION

Lean is about pull and flow – the third and fourth lean principles. The vision is that parts and products flow like a river whose volume matches the demand rate. Gradually, the flow erodes the loops and finds short cuts, so that lengths decrease and problem rocks are worn away. With time, dams and lakes along the route are made to disappear, so progress downstream is not delayed. Shortening the flow length means that flow can be even and does not have to be released early in anticipation of uncertain demand.

KANBAN

Kanban is suitable for any type of repetitive manufacture, and variations may be suitable for non-repetitive. A kanban works between a pair of workstations only. Parts are pulled by the next workstation only as needed, and the supplier workstation stops work if no parts are pulled. This prevents overproduction and synchronises operations. Ultimately only the main build is scheduled, with all subassemblies and components being pulled in as needed.

There are two general types of kanban. The product type signals for an identical part or batch to be replaced. A sequence kanban signals that a

Lean: PULL and SYNCHRONISATION

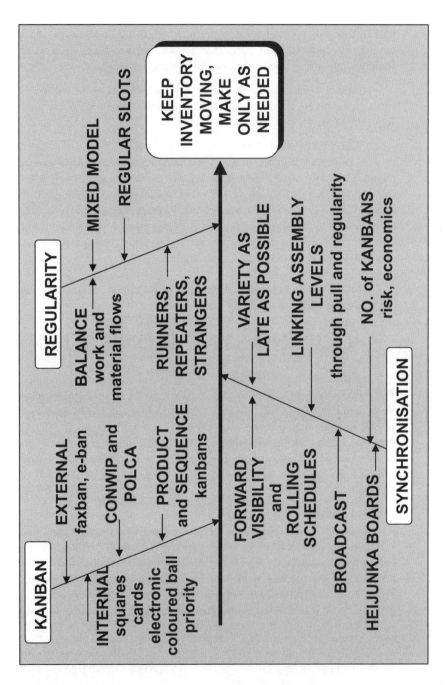

workstation is ready for more work, but the actual part to be made is determined by a list or broadcast (see below). Kanban can work internally or externally. Internally, kanban squares are the most simple type: when empty, fill it; when full do not make more. Kanban cards may be single or dual. The far more common single card is a physical signal to make a replacement. No card, no make. Variations include "ping pong ball" which are sent ahead of assembly to signal the preparation of a part which will be completed just in time to be inserted. Priority kanbans are simply pull cards but with colours to indicate urgency. Parts are pulled in order green, yellow, red but replenished in the reverse order. The batch made may be red only, or red and yellow, or red, yellow and green. An alternative accumulates cards in a column until a trip point is reached signifying that production must commence. Dual card kanban has production cards and move cards and allows finer tuning and different move and make quantities. Electronic versions can be displayed. Externally, physical cards can be used but so too can faxban or e-ban.

A Heijunka (level production) board authorises production in (say) 10 minute slots. The board is loaded up with the mix of products, and of course is visible.

The number of kanbans and parts in a loop depends upon stock-out risk, lead-time, part cost, and material handling. (You would not be prepared to make excessive replenishments of a low cost item, and more kanbans protect against lead-time uncertainty). Normally, start "slack" and gradually tighten.

CONWIP is a kanban-like system that maintains a constant amount of WIP by releasing only an amount of work equal to that completed. By comparison with conventional kanban, less WIP is made possible and buffers can "float". The penalty is visibility. POLCA (by Rajan Suri) is a kanban system that signals the supplier workcentre from completion at the next workstation (rather than from the start as with normal kanban). This ensures that work is released only when a clear path is apparent. POLCA may be used in job shop operations. POLCA cards are released as late as possible.

SYNCHRONISATION.
The aim is to keep materials moving – keeping people and a machine moving is less important. But do not allow materials to move faster than customer demand – work at the takt time. Unfortunately seasonality and acquire-and-make lead times longer than customer expectations are a fact

Lean and MEASUREMENT

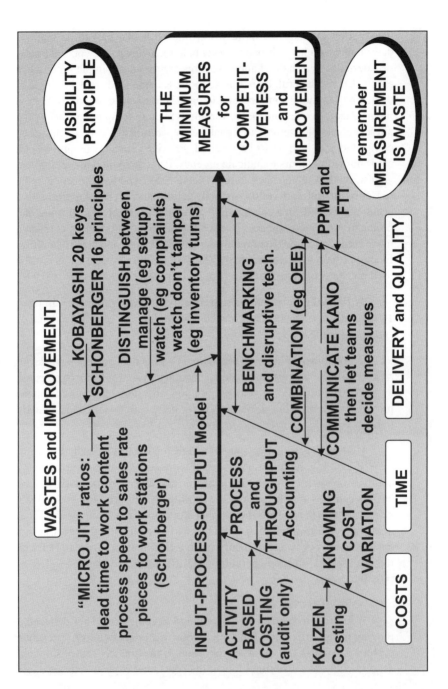

VISIBILITY PRINCIPLE

THE MINIMUM MEASURES for COMPETIT-IVENESS and IMPROVEMENT

remember MEASUREMENT IS WASTE

WASTES and IMPROVEMENT

KOBAYASHI 20 keys

SCHONBERGER 16 principles

DISTINGUISH between manage (eg setup) watch (eg complaints) watch don't tamper (eg inventory turns)

"MICRO JIT" ratios: lead time to work content process speed to sales rate pieces to work stations (Schonberger)

INPUT-PROCESS-OUTPUT Model

BENCHMARKING and disruptive tech.

COMBINATION (eg OEE)

COMMUNICATE KANO then let teams decide measures

PPM and FTT

PROCESS and THROUGHPUT Accounting

KNOWING COST VARIATION

ACTIVITY BASED COSTING (audit only)

KAIZEN Costing

COSTS

TIME

DELIVERY and QUALITY

of life. So while attacking lead times by all the techniques in this book, aim to add value as late as possible. Seek lower level commonality or platforms. This is why design is such a powerful weapon for better schedules. Forward visibility and rolling schedules aim to clarify expectations both internally and externally. Change as little as possible. Internally, the broadcast system is used in car plants and elsewhere where several assemblies need to synchronise. Broadcast launches each branch in exactly the right sequence.

Regularity aims at a "no surprises: schedule. In batch production, try to make the same products at about the same time every day or every week. This helps maintenance, changeovers, suppliers, tooling, and workforce. In assembly, aim for mixed model production (a repeating sequence of mixed products all day rather than A in morning, B in afternoon.) This allows smooth, continuous flow.

MEASUREMENT

Measurement is a necessary waste with lean and supply chain, so the minimum necessary actions should be sought. Measurement should be set and taken with the participation of those being measured. They should be at the appropriate level (where something can be done about it). And measures should be made visible and kept at "gemba".

WASTES AND IMPROVEMENT
Self-audit measures are useful. Kobayashi's 20 keys allow self-rating in 20 shop floor oriented areas, on a 1 to 5 scale. Schonberger's 16 Principles are an alternative applicable throughout the enterprise and supply chain. In related work, Schonberger talks about three levels of measures. The first are those (such as quality, delivery, and changeover) that can be influenced on a day to day basis and should be measured on a day to day basis. At the next level are measures that result from performance in these day to day activities. Complaints are an example. These, like SPC, should not be tampered in the short term except when special causes are apparent. And on yet a higher level measures such as inventory turns and costs are even more indirect and should be regarded as the outcome of lower level actions, and not set directly. Statistical thinking.

Schonberger also suggests three "micro JIT ratios" for a quick audit. The ideal ratio of each measure should be 1 but is typically hundreds of times higher. A challenge.

The input-process-output model uses these three areas plus design and innovation, financial outcomes, and environment, to give six clear areas for lean and supply chain measurement. This is an alternative "balanced scorecard" arguably more direct than the original.

COSTS.

The lean approach to costing is to simplify and measure the least possible. Eliminate rather than measure. Variances are generally waste – see above. However, accountants should be aware of cost variations within a single product – for example, how much does variation in lead time or inventory affect the costs of a product. Activity Based Costing (ABC) gives better answers than traditional overhead and standard costing but is far too complex to be used other than on a check or audit basis. Process Accounting is more in line with the lean ideal of flow. Throughput accounting concentrates on direct costs and may use lead-time as a basis to allocate overheads.

Kaizen costing concentrates on improvement goals rather than on actual costs. In fact, actual costs may not even be measured.

TIME, DELIVERY, QUALITY

Time is perhaps the single most important measure in lean and supply chain. This is because it directly influences customer satisfaction and indirectly all of the seven wastes (see section on improvement). So give time achievement and reduction a prime place in measurement systems.

A central core of measures are time, cost, quality, delivery, service, and morale – although cost should not be directly measured. Beware once again of over-reacting to natural variation. Statistical thinking.

Benchmarking is useful, but be careful to target specific measures, not to go in for industrial tourism. Take particular notice of what Christensen calls "disruptive technologies" – ideas that are treated as a joke but come to dominate, such as the PC, the steel mini-mill, or indeed Lean manufacturing. Be aware of the Kano factors (basics, performance, and delighters).

Combination measures such as OEE (availability x performance x quality), delivery (on time x quantity x quality), total satisfaction (right product x when needed x right quantity) are useful "shotgun" measures to get to root causes.

Use parts per million measures of defects, but also first time through.

Supply Chain

LEAN SUPPLY

The Supply Chain emerged as a major force for competitiveness during the 1990s, but supplier partnership is much older. Most companies have supply chains and distribution chains. These work together with internal processes. Improving cost, quality, delivery and service is what supply chain co-operation is all about. This requires that all members of the chain, end to end, supply to distribution, adopt lean principles, six sigma principles and supply chain principles. Of course this is a long task.

The marriage analogy is appropriate. Marriage is for the longer term. It is based on trust and mutual respect. It will have its ups and downs, but with give and take both are better off. Marriage involves commitment to a single partner, not playing the field.

COST REDUCTION

The first principle is buying on cost not price. Cost is a far wider concept including quality, reliability, and delivery. Supply cost reduction has several strands. Target costing, used often with value engineering, has both internal and supplier implications. Target cost = market price – profit. This leads to the "allowable cost" for products and components. Achieving component costs sets a target for suppliers, that are assisted by company personnel. Several methods discussed in the Design section are relevant. Target costing may extend to "chained target costing" whereby various tiers in a supply chain co-operate to achieve target costs at their own respective levels. There may be several of these chains, and the exercise may begin half way down a chain, not necessarily at the final product stage.

Design co-operation calls for suppliers to participate in, or take over, design for which they have particular expertise. With trust, wastes between the partners can be identified and eliminated – examples include double buffers, inspection, billing. The ideal is delivery to the point of use, under pull, with perfect quality. Waste reduction is achieved by sharing expertise, and joint teams, on all topics in this book. This is "win-win" for both parties – security, confidence to invest, and low cost. Risk is reduced because there is too much to lose. Of course, this is only possible with fewer suppliers, so a process of selecting partners must begin. Holding "supplier

Lean SUPPLY

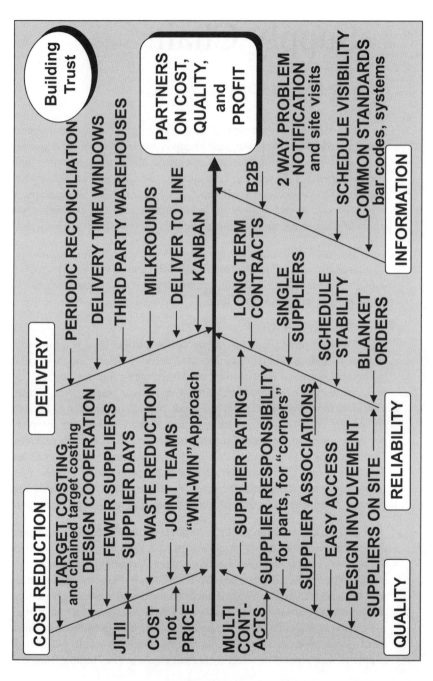

days" to explain expectations should be periodic. For some, JITII is a possibility whereby premier supplier's representatives work at the company site writing purchase orders on their own company and co-operating with product development.

QUALITY

Ideally suppliers should deliver perfect quality direct to the point of use without the necessity for inspection. Historically only purchasing spoke to purchasing; now there are multiple points of contact – quality to quality, scheduling to scheduling, design to design. Increasingly suppliers are asked to take over responsibility for larger assemblies (or 'corners') not just components. Quality is a prime reason, but cost, expertise, and control are other reasons. At some automotive plants this extends to having suppliers employees actually doing the assembly on the final product site. Improving quality involves working more closely with supplier designers, not only first tier. Easy access to design and process information encourages trust, reduces cost, and improves awareness of requirements. Supplier Associations have become a major means of fostering improved supplier performance. These are "clubs", often sponsored by a major customer, which co-operate by sharing expertise and resources and solving mutual problems. Other types co-operate within a region.

RELIABILITY

Quality and delivery reliability is frequently measured by a rating scheme. Poor suppliers get dropped; good suppliers win more business and long term contracts. Such contracts, combined with single or few suppliers encourage good performance. One practice is to develop two good suppliers for a major component and then to award one of them life-of-the-product business. Another product may see the second supplier winning. Schedule stability is encouraged by demand management practices (see separate section) and blanket orders.

DELIVERY

The lean delivery ideal is direct to the line via kanban pull in small batches. Milkrounds, delivering several components in small batches instead of one component in a larger batch makes this economic. Fewer suppliers, supplying more parts also help make this cost effective. Delivery is within specific time windows, and periodic reconciliation (or even self-billing) rather than invoicing cuts costs. A third party warehouse or in-house supermarket, from where parts are delivered to the line in small batches, but received in larger batches may be an interim solution.

71

Lean DISTRIBUTION

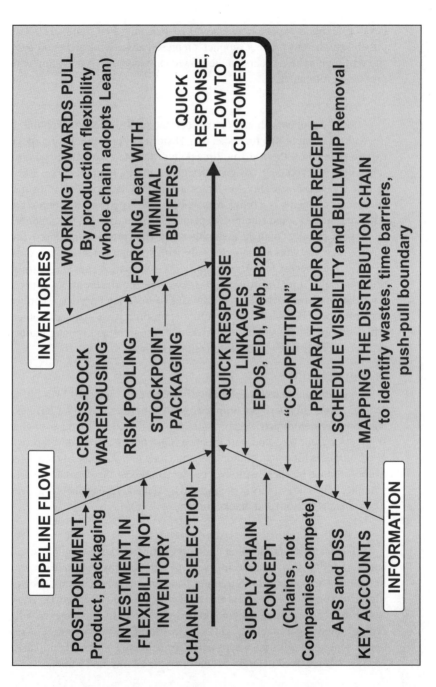

INFORMATION

Is the glue that welds suppliers. Schedule visibility is a goal, sometimes electronic through the web. Common standards on bar codes, computer systems, and containers help. So does two-way problem notification whereby each side gives maximum warning of any disruption. Site visits by all manner of personnel, from operator to CEO, assist understanding and can cut duplication wastes.

LEAN DISTRIBUTION

Distribution is the other half of the supply chain. The aim is to achieve quick response, pipeline flow with minimum waste. In reality many distribution systems are networks catering for particular customer types along selected channels. Today it is recognised that supply chains compete, not companies.

PIPELINE FLOW

The idea is flow, not warehousing which is waste. Cross docking shifts products from one truck to several delivery vehicles, so that inventory is warehoused for hours not days or weeks. Flow is aided by selecting appropriate channels; perhaps one for large customers, another for fast moving, a third for small customers. Flow may be aided by postponement in product (assembling at the last moment) or packaging (by customer type or language). A general principle is investment in flexibility rather than inventory; for instance in changeover, in transport, in capacity.

INVENTORY

The ideal is to supply no-more and no-less, working under pull not push. This can only be achieved by a long-term end-to-end effort along the chain in the adoption of lean techniques and principles. Forcing lean by insisting on minimal buffers prevents game playing and amplification effects, and encourages the chain to work at the customer's rate. Where warehousing is necessary "Risk Pooling" whereby local warehouse inventory is centralised and local warehouses closed, results in less inventory. Although inventory reduction takes place the penalty may be in response time. However, inventory and other flexibility savings may mean that more costly quick distribution still pays.

Stockpoint packaging tries to minimise the costs of stacking shelves and material handling by packing product in final display form, perhaps on roller pallets.

INFORMATION

Is key. Quick Response linkages with EPOS terminals or internet allow true customer demands to be communicated. B2B e-business is uncovering huge opportunity for speed and waste reduction. Related is schedule visibility, schedule stability and removal of the "bullwhip" effect which can also lead to huge savings. See the separate section on demand management. An associated step is to map the supply or distribution chain, particularly to identify wastes and the point where Push meets Pull – and how it can be made to move upstream in future. The "co-opetition" concept allows competitors to co-operate for mutual benefit against outsiders but still to compete. Examples are common standards, trains vs. airlines, national distribution vs. international competition. Preparation for order receipt is a form of changeover reduction in distribution whereby maximum preparation for both physical and information flows are made in advance of receipt. Examples are customs pre-clearance and synchronised operations with fruit picking. Key account management extends the supplier partnership concepts to key customers. Both sides win.

Scheduling software, decision support (DSS), and advanced production scheduling (APS) is generally not favoured in lean manufacturing, except sometimes for planning, but in distribution it certainly has a place to optimise warehouse location, inventory management, and cross docking.

Lean DESIGN and DEVELOPMENT

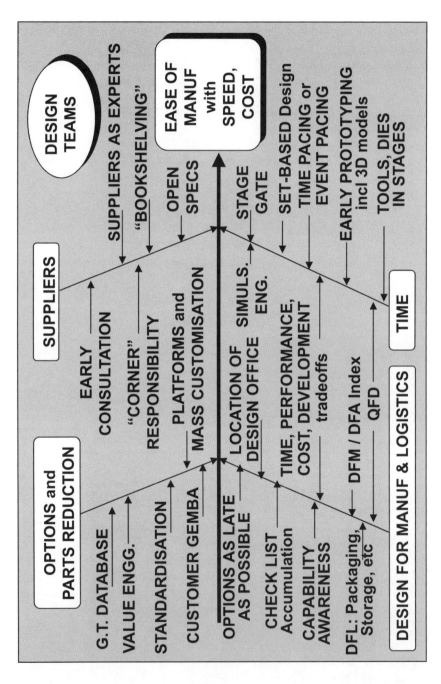

Wider Systems

LEAN DESIGN & DEVELOPMENT

It is said that 80% of costs become locked in at the design stage. But that is only a part of the picture. Design is the major factor in many product sales. Time to market, an increasingly important feature of competitiveness is strongly influenced by the design stage. This is a summary of what can be done.

OPTIONS and PARTS REDUCTION
Many designers begin design by consulting a group technology or similar database. They are looking for similar products and components. They also wish to use standard parts to minimise inventory proliferation. Value engineering, either to improve value at same cost or reduce cost by retaining characteristics, is a team activity done before manufacture. VE uses functional analysis to identify the basic functions and then uses creative thinking to simplify. Standardisation weighs the cost of providing a feature to all products against the complexity costs of inventory and scheduling by providing it as an option.

Going to "gemba", as usual, is desirable. For example sending the concept team to live in the customer market for three months, or speaking directly to customers.

Platforms have emerged as a major concept in automotive, now extending to other products. Two calculators may look different but underlying they share the same platform and a majority of components. Mass Customisation attempts to gain the advantages of the assembly line but for customised products. This is done by modularity, postponement, late packaging, re-sequencing (e.g. Benetton dying jerseys after not before manufacture), point of sale configuration (Dell computer), or several of these.

DESIGN for MANUFACTURE and LOGISTICS
Options as late as possible, as used in mass customisation, can have a dramatic impact on inventory and flexibility. Throughout design and development, and with market feedback, an effective simple technique

used by Toyota is to keep checklists that effectively accumulate experience for future products. Design should always be done with knowledge of manufacturing capability. Locating the design office as near to assembly as possible assists this. The effectiveness of design for manufacture (DFA) and design for assembly (DFA) may be measured by an index developed by Boothroyd and Dewhurst. In the design process four important variables are time, product performance, product cost, and development. The interconnections represent six tradeoffs that should be explicitly made (Smith and Reinertson). Quality Function Deployment (QFD) is a major technique for design and development teams, which systematically integrates the "voice of the customer", benchmarking, comparative products, and product features. Design for Logistics can lead to big savings by incorporating packaging, storage, vehicle compatibility, and recycling considerations for conditions to be encountered along the distribution chain.

SUPPLIERS

Working with suppliers on product design is increasing. This uses early consultation with suppliers having focused expertise and who may be responsible for whole "corners", not just parts. The "open spec" concept aids this by giving suppliers the minimum possible spec to allow maximum innovation. Bookshelving is where co-operation with a supplier leads to technical advance that is stored for future use but which can be incorporated very quickly.

TIME

Design time can be reduced by simultaneous engineering, rather than sequential over-the-wall, concepts. Here the multi-discipline design team works together under a project leader who can call in functional expertise as required. The stage gate approach involves identifying definite stages that the whole team works towards, and at which a "go / no-go" decision is made. Set-based design works on major assemblies simultaneously, but deliberately keeping options open as late as possible. The options are slowly reduced. A similar approach is adopted with tools and dies, acquiring and machining as far as possible at each stage but cutting the last metal very soon after the design is finalised. Early prototyping and the use of 3D resin models aid assembly design and part matching. Event paced design proceeds at a pace dictated by the project plan, but time paced design uses the lean principle of regularity to introduce new products (microchips, chocolate bars) with a certain paced regularity, which has resource and capacity advantages. Mapping the design process can be a revelation.

CUSTOMER SERVICE

Today manufacturing and service are bundled. This is crucial for manufacturers and everyone involved in supply chains to realise. There are two aspects – winning customers and retaining them. It is one supply chain and its product-service package against another, rather than one manufacturer and its products against another. And everyone is involved.

WINNING CUSTOMERS

Winning customers involves, first and foremost, understanding customer value. Value is product and service performance divided by cost. "You don't sell customers a product but a benefit" is an old marketing idea but valued benefits are hard to identify. One way is surely to extend the lean principles of visibility, of gemba, of involvement, of partnership and passing on the benefits, of clear communication, out to customers. And who is a customer? (Final, intermediate, supply chain, or all?)

Winning customers by word of mouth may involve "memorable experiences"; mere satisfaction is no longer good enough. Exceeding expectations – what Kano refers to as "delighters" – is something to strive for, but for lean, six sigma and supply chain, delivering superior results on the performance factors is as important.

One way is to map the sequence of customer interface activities (or "moments of truth") and for each to ensure that (a) "basics" are met (b) performance is superior (c) delighters (or WOW! factors) are provided whenever economically possible (d) standards – and consistency - are adhered to, and (e) where possible actions are failsafed or error proofed. So instead of looking for value add and non value add activities as would be done internally, interpret the word "value" in wider terms from the customer perspective. Note that the sequence of activities begins with the customer thinking about buying and only ends when the product is finally disposed of.

Another way is to pass on the time benefits of lean and supply chain - in other words to reduce lead times and allow customers to cut their own inventories and become more agile. This strengthens the supply chain.

The "Service Profit Chain" is a phrase coined by Sasser at Harvard to illustrate the systems thinking nature of good service. Good company

Lean CUSTOMER SERVICE

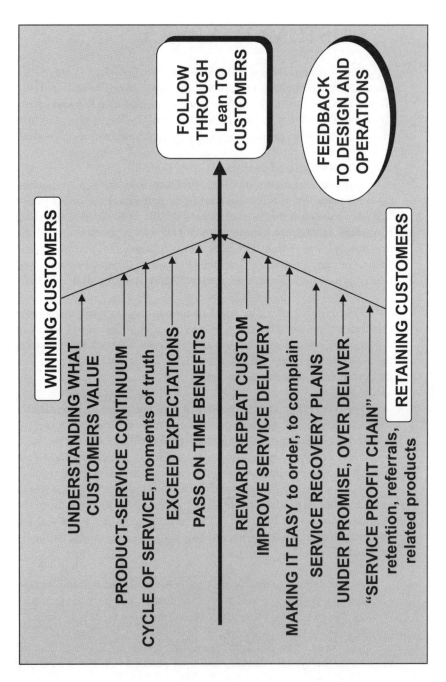

WINNING CUSTOMERS

UNDERSTANDING WHAT CUSTOMERS VALUE

PRODUCT-SERVICE CONTINUUM

CYCLE OF SERVICE, moments of truth

EXCEED EXPECTATIONS

PASS ON TIME BENEFITS

REWARD REPEAT CUSTOM

IMPROVE SERVICE DELIVERY

MAKING IT EASY to order, to complain

SERVICE RECOVERY PLANS

UNDER PROMISE, OVER DELIVER

"SERVICE PROFIT CHAIN" retention, referrals, related products

RETAINING CUSTOMERS

FOLLOW THROUGH Lean TO CUSTOMERS

FEEDBACK TO DESIGN AND OPERATIONS

policies towards employees result in motivated employees. Motivated employees, together with supportive service policies allow good service to be delivered. Good service delivery results in customer satisfaction. Customer satisfaction results in repeat business. Which means more profit to support good employee policies. The 3 R's of service are retention, referrals, and related products that together form a powerful feedback loop.

RETAINING CUSTOMERS
Today the benefits of retaining customers are better understood. ("It costs five times as much to win a new customer as it does to retain an existing one", and "benefits of retained customers continue to accrue with minimal promotion year after year".) So reward repeat custom by sharing the benefits. Good service delivery means closing the gaps (described by Zeithaml in "Delivering Quality Service") between (a) expected service perceptions of customer expectations (b) perceptions of customer expectations and service specifications (c) service specifications and service delivery, and (d) service delivery and communications about the service. This of course implies measuring the extent of each gap. A good policy is to under-promise (on delivery time, product performance, and service backup) but over-deliver rather than the reverse.

Because some things are still bound to go wrong (despite standardisation which is a pre-requisite), have a good service recovery plan prepared in advance. Research has shown that excellent service recovery not only retains custom, but also builds loyalty. The aim is not only to restore confidence, but also to limit the possibility of it happening again. It's continuous improvement.

Measure service performance, not mere satisfaction. For example a supermarket measure is having the correct product (no substitutes), in the required quantity, when needed.

SUSTAINABLE LEAN

Ultimate lean means sustainable lean. Ultimate lean means no waste in the "wider systems" of energy, materials, and pollution.

5R's
The book *Natural Capitalism* by Hawkins, Lovins and Lovins (Little, Brown, 2000) gives scores of exciting examples how products can profitably

SUSTAINABLE Lean

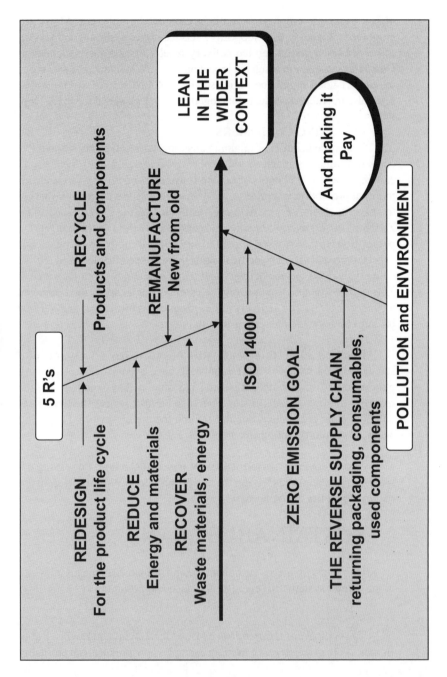

meet both environmental and performance objectives. Product design for the life cycle, including packaging during shipment, durability, ease of maintenance, ease of upgrading, the repair cycle, and ultimate disposal makes products more competitive. Customers, like good supplier partnership practice, are looking at total cost not just price. Likewise the reduction of energy and materials both during manufacture and in use makes for improved competitiveness. The recovery of waste materials during manufacture has long been promoted in good manufacturing companies. Perhaps less common is the recovery and use of packaging and energy conservation in the plant, the office, and in distribution. Similar remarks can be made for recycling. Both recovery and recycling need to begin at the design stage – whether for a product or for a factory. The former is more common, even trendy but the latter is more unusual. Finally "re-man" is a growing trend with a lean manufacturing expertise of its own.

POLLUTION AND ENVIRONMENT

It is no news that environmental concerns are increasingly important. ISO14000 embodied these in a standard and several corporations have zero emission goals. More unusually, engineering the reverse supply chain, where a company takes responsibility for the return of packaging, consumables and used components will surely grow. Make it pay.

Lean IMPLEMENTATION

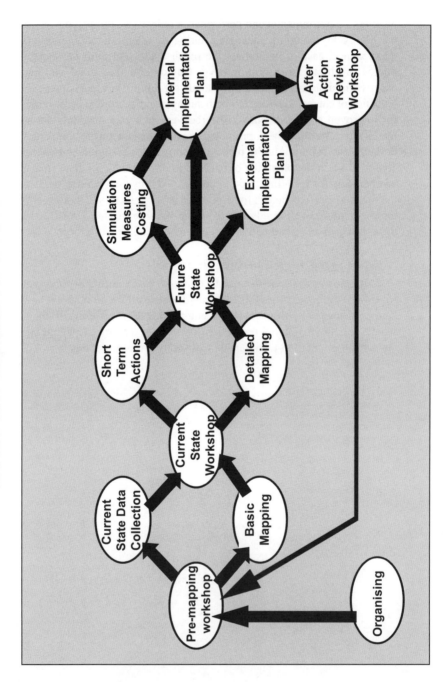

Lean Implementation

ORGANISING

Comprises selecting a steering committee, establishing a Lean Promotion Office (a war office with resources), selecting the lean champion (preferably full time), and lean implementation teams including shop floor staff. Consult the union. Gain agreement.

PRE-MAPPING WORKSHOP

To customer values, identify key processes, product contribution analyses and contribution per bottleneck minute information. Also to discuss capacity issues and constraints, identify processes, products and routings to be mapped, and to select appropriate data collection periods and frequency. What information flows need to be mapped?

CURRENT STATE DATA COLLECTION

May comprise a situation audit (Kobayashi or Schonberger), and audits of housekeeping status and schedule adherence. Check OEE, standards and inventory record accuracy, delivery performance. Review the measures used and costing system. Collect takt time information. Check on process and schedule variation, and list the possible causes.

BASIC MAPPING

Will include current state "learning to see" maps, spaghetti diagrams, quality filter charts, and demand amplification. Mapping to be done by operators and staff, not the "experts".

CURRENT STATE WORKSHOP

Present maps and data. Consider possibilities for flow. Check size of buffers and necessity for supermarkets. What are the barriers to pull? How can visibility be improved? Examine existing cell performance and new cells. What are feasible production schedules? One-piece flow? Identify "low hanging fruit" and areas for more detailed study.

SHORT TERM ACTIONS

Probably 5S and changeover, standardisation, possibly selected kaizen blitz events. Identification of short term six sigma and quality improvement projects.

BASIC MAPPING TOOLS

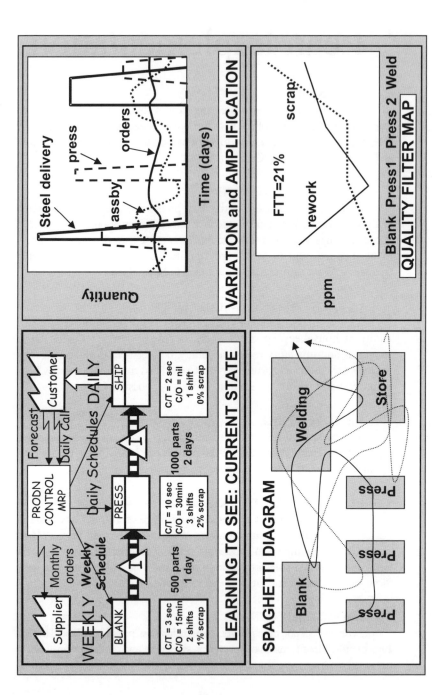

VARIATION and AMPLIFICATION

FTT=21%

scrap

rework

ppm

Blank Press1 Press 2 Weld

QUALITY FILTER MAP

Steel delivery

press

assby

orders

Time (days)

Quantity

Forecast

Customer

PRODN
CONTROL
MRP

Supplier

Monthly
orders

WEEKLY Weekly
Schedule

Daily Call

Daily Schedules DAILY

BLANK

C/T = 3 sec
C/O = 15min
2 shifts
1% scrap

500 parts
1 day

PRESS

C/T = 10 sec
C/O = 30min
3 shifts
2% scrap

1000 parts
2 days

SHIP

C/T = 2 sec
C/O = nil
1 shift
0% scrap

LEARNING TO SEE: CURRENT STATE

SPAGHETTI DIAGRAM

Welding

Store

Press

Press

Press

Blank

DETAILED MAPPING AND DATA

Use process activity maps selectively. Probably map information flows and possibly new product introduction. More detail on scheduling. Spend time on collecting variation data.

FUTURE STATE WORKSHOP

Develop the concept. Consider location. Detailed layout and sizing of supermarkets and buffers. Detailed work on the schedule, including the pacemaker process, batch sizing. Kanban implementation plan.

SIMULATION, MEASURES AND COSTING

Possibly small scale trials, scale models. Perhaps even computer simulation. Revise and simplify the costing system. Examine the measures used.

INTERNAL IMPLEMENTATION PLAN

Phasing of layout and cell changes. Activities leading to inventory reductions and phased removal of barriers to flow. Operator skill development. Six Sigma project phasing. Develop other plans, probably TPM and information flow. "Small machine" policy.

EXTERNAL IMPLEMENTATION PLAN

Plans to reduce demand amplification. Supplier reduction and development. Supplier associations. Sharing information and working towards stable schedules. Phasing in of pull. Other actions such as joint design, B2B, JITII, chained target costing.

Do it all again!

You are on the road but you are never there. Best wishes on your journey!

Further Reading

The following is a personal selection of the best

Lean
John Bicheno, *The Lean Toolbox*, PICSIE Books, 2000. Much fuller explanations of materials on Lean than in this booklet.
Richard Schonberger, *Japanese Manufacturing Techniques*, Free Press, 1982. Still the most readable introduction, and yes, 1982!
James Womack and Daniel Jones, *Lean Thinking*, Simon and Schuster, 1996. The five principles and good cases.
John Nicholas, *Competitive Manufacturing Management*, McGraw Hill, 1998. The best "blockbuster" text on Lean (840 pages).

Supply Chain
David Simchi-Levi et al, *Designing and Managing the Supply Chain*, Mc Graw Hill, 2000
Robin Cooper and Regine Slagmulder, *Supply Chain Development for the Lean Enterprise*, Productivity / IMA, 1999

Six Sigma
Mikel Harry and Richard Schroder, *Six Sigma*, ASQ Press, 2000

Best Magazine
Target, published by Association for Manufacturing Excellence (AME)

Web Sites
www.cf.ac.uk\carbs\lerc
www.ame.org
www.lean.org